6-26-64

Agricultural Bargaining Power

Agricultural

Bargaining

Power

GEORGE W. LADD

Professor of Economics
Iowa State University
Ames, Iowa

IOWA STATE UNIVERSITY PRESS

Ames, IOWA, U.S.A.

About the author. . .

GEORGE W. LADD is professor of Economics at Iowa State University. A native of South Dakota, he was graduated from South Dakota State College in 1950. He earned the M.A. degree from Michigan State University and the Ph.D. degree from the University of Illinois. He taught at Southern Illinois University and has been on the staff of Iowa State University since 1955. Dr. Ladd's work has been published in reports of the Center for Agricultural and Economic Development and of the Iowa Agricultural and Home Economics Experiment Station; in *Journal of Farm Economics* and other professional journals; and in poultry trade magazines.

Library of Congress catalog card number: 63-22162

Preface

THIS BOOK is a contribution from the Iowa Agricultural and Home Economics Experiment Station as a collaborator under North Central Regional cooperative research project "Changing Market Structure and Organization of the Midwest Dairy Industry." The financial support of the Iowa Agricultural and Home Economics Experiment Station and North Central Regional Research Funds is gratefully acknowledged.

Many of my colleagues in the Department of Economics and Sociology at Iowa State University contributed in one way or another to this book. My initial work on agricultural bargaining was done in collaboration with J. Robert Strain. The whole book reflects his influence, exercised through our initial collaboration, through many subsequent discussions, and through his review of the manuscript. Harold Davey provided me an education in labor economics. His suggestions on that part of the manuscript dealing with labor unions resulted in a number of improvements in the text. Joe Bohlen read the sections dealing with group dynamics. Comments of Everett Stoneberg and Lee Kolmer greatly improved the organization and presentation. Discussions with Robert Rizek and Errol Petersen were helpful. Work of collecting basic data presented in charts and tables was performed by Milton Hallberg. My sincere thanks to all these people.

I also wish to thank the authors and publishers who so kindly permitted me to quote their works.

GEORGE W. LADD
Ames, Iowa

Table of Contents

Agricultural Bargaining Power

Introduction

AGRICULTURAL BARGAINING POWER is a popular topic among farmers and farm organizations. Farmers see the prices they receive going downward and the prices they pay trending upward. They observe concentrations of economic power in the hands of big labor and big business. They see a possibility of increasing their own economic power through widespread use of bargaining associations. Some feel that farmers may use bargaining power to solve their own problems and "get the government out of agriculture." Farm organizations that strongly disagree on most aspects of agricultural policy agree on the desirability of increasing farmers' bargaining power.

How can farmers obtain bargaining power and use it to improve their prices? Before we can answer this question we need to bring together facts and ideas pertaining to agricultural bargaining. The object of this book is to present material to help you make sound decisions concerning agricultural bargaining. If you are a member of a bargaining association this material will help you see what you can do to strengthen your association. If you are a member of a group attempting to form a bargaining association or if you are trying to make up your mind about joining or forming an organization, the material should be helpful to you.

Chapter 2 is essentially definitional. It defines bargain and bargaining power and looks at the two different types of bargaining power. This is followed by a discussion of the sources of bargaining gains: reductions in marketing costs and increases in prices to consumers. Chapter 4, devoted to bargaining power and supply control, presents a discussion of a serious problem facing organizations that rely solely on raising selling prices to enhance farm incomes. This is followed by a discussion of the conditions an organization will have to meet to possess and exercise bargaining power. Chapter 7 is a discussion of special problems in the attainment of unity, one of the organizational conditions. Agricultural bargaining associations face many of the same problems labor unions have faced. Labor union growth was stimulated by favorable legislation enacted in the 1930's. Chapter 8 shows the role this legislation played in stimulating union growth. This chapter also relates marketing order legislation to bargaining power. The next chapter analyzes the principal forces that determine the outcome of a bargaining process. Chapter 10 shows how unions have continuously had to adjust their structure to maintain or enhance their bargaining power. The final chapter is a summary chapter.

Bargaining Power

A BARGAIN is an advantageous agreement. To bargain means to buy or sell on good terms, to haggle, to negotiate and compromise. Power, on the other hand, is the possession of influence over others; the ability to bring about change. Bargaining power is the combination of these: the ability to bargain with influence to bring about a desired change.

Between parties in a bargaining process, there is an opposing conflict of interest but also a common interest. Auto manufacturers and the automobile workers' union, for example, have a common interest in producing and selling more cars. But they have a conflict of interest in the way money spent for cars should be divided between workers and company. The underlying common interest is seldom forgotten by either—even though their behavior at the bargaining table may suggest differently.

Likewise, livestock producers and packers have a common interest in producing and selling more meat to consumers at satisfactory prices. They have a conflict of interest because each wants a larger share of the consumer's meat dollar.

[13]

In the bargaining process, each party seeks an agreement advantageous to him. He will use bargaining power and negotiating skill. At each stage of a bargaining process, each party is faced with three choices: (1) to accept the other party's latest offer (2) to reject this offer or (3) to reject the offer but try to get more favorable terms. A bargain is reached when the parties agree on terms. At each stage of the bargaining, each party will be considering, "If I make choice (1), what will happen to me after the bargaining is over? What will happen if I choose (2)? How about (3)?"

WHAT IS BARGAINING POWER

Bargaining power is the ability to influence the results the other party will experience if he makes the first or second choice. The more favorable you can make it for him to accept your offer or the more unfavorable you can make it for him if he refuses to accept and refuses to bargain further, the greater is your bargaining power.

There are, then, two kinds of bargaining power. The first stems from advantages that can be offered to the other party for accepting your terms. The second stems from the ability to make the other party worse off if he does not accept your offer.

Type I Bargaining Power

For agriculture, the first kind of influence requires enough farmers so organized that they can offer savings or some other advantages to the person or firm from whom they desire concessions. Farm supply cooperatives — through mass buying of feeds, seeds, fertilizers, gasoline, etc — can offer suppliers gains from lower marketing costs and more assured outlets than if the suppliers served each member separately. If a supplier is willing to share part of this gain as a quantity discount, coop members can obtain supplies at lower cost.

Farm marketing associations organized on a large enough scale also can offer the other party gains that he may be persuaded to share. A grade A milk bargaining association, for example, may be able to offer procurement services at lower cost than several bottlers could achieve by acting separately. Possibilities include producer check writing, quality control, product standardization, fat tests, checking for antibiotics and the field work necessary for these services.

A full-supply contract specifying time and place of delivery relieves a bottler of the cost and trouble of finding extra sources of milk when the supply is short or of disposing of surplus milk when it is in excess supply. In return, bottlers may sign contracts which assure members of an outlet that will not be cut off at will by the bottler. Advantages provided by the association may also permit higher returns for milk supplied by members.

If all the grade A milk producers supplying one bottler convert from can handling to bulk handling of milk, the bottler will be able to reduce costs of receiving and cooling milk. A 1957 study indicated that in the midwest these savings could run from 5 to 22 cents per hundredweight of milk received.[1] There will be further savings to the plant if the conversion from can to bulk handling is accompanied by a shift from every day to every other day pickup of milk. Then savings can amount to between 15 and 32 cents per hundredweight of milk received. Hence, if all members of a grade A milk producers' co-op will agree to convert to bulk, the co-op will be able to bargain over how much of the savings the bottler can keep and how much must be paid out as bulk milk premiums.

There are distinct seasonal variations in consumer demand for several foods: beef, pork, eggs, fluid milk and broilers, among others. Another possibility for exercising Type I bargaining power may exist in the adjustment of seasonal patterns of farm marketings to mesh more closely with seasonal variations in consumer demand. For example, the demand for broilers is lowest in December, rises to a peak in July and then falls until

---

[1]Donald B. Agnew, *How Bulk Assembly Changes Milk Marketing Costs,* USDA Marketing Research Rept. 190, 1957, pp. 17—18.

December. If the quantity of broilers marketed in July and August were to remain constant at the December level of marketings, July and August farm broiler prices would be about 35 percent higher than December prices.[2] To achieve these higher prices and added income, farmers might have to alter their seasonal marketings; processing and marketing firms might have to change their operations somewhat. If, through organization action, producers fitted their pattern of marketing more closely to consumer demand, an organization could bargain with these firms concerning how the additional income would be divided among firms and farmers.

At a conference of fruit and vegetable bargaining cooperatives, A. C. Moll of the Stokely-Van Camp canning company suggested four specific ways in which organizations of growers might aid in bringing about cost reductions which could result in increased returns to growers: [3]

1. Elimination of processor services not economically productive and assumption by growers of growing and delivery functions which can be done at lower cost by the grower.
2. Mechanization of harvesting through processor or custom-operated specialized equipment not feasible for the individual grower, thereby accomplishing reductions in cost.
3. Improvement of raw product quality with reference to costs of preparation, percentage of recoverable finished product, and sales value of the finished product.
4. Improved scheduling of production for maximum efficiency.

Examples of this type of power can be found in places other than farming. Some unions operate employment services or "hiring halls" to help businessmen find workers and to help members find jobs. This relieves businessmen of some or all expenses in obtaining employees. Businessmen may be willing to pay for this

---

[2] Richard D. Darley and Paul L. Farris, "Stabilizing the Broiler Industry," *Economic and Marketing Information for Indiana Farmers,* Purdue Univ. Agr. Ext. Serv., Sept. 30, 1961.

[3] A. C. Moll, "A Processors View of Bargaining Associations," *Proceedings of the 4th National Conference on Fruit and Vegetable Bargaining Cooperatives,* USDA Farmer Coop. Serv., Jan. 4, 1960, p. 40.

service by paying higher wages. Management also may gain through labor contracts providing for arbitration, rather than strikes as a final means of settling disputes. This may make management willing to pay higher wages.

Type II Bargaining Power

The first kind of bargaining power makes it advantageous for the other party to accept your offer. If he does not accept, he is no better off than before, but no worse off either. The second kind of bargaining power, however, can make him worse off.

Even though an organization has bargaining skill and Type I power, it may not be able to obtain any of the resulting savings for its members unless it also has the second kind of bargaining power. In case the organization cannot or will not offer offsetting savings or advantages to the other party, it *must* have the second kind of power if it is to obtain concessions such as higher selling prices or lower buying prices for its members.

An organization with Type II power has the ability to subject the other party to added costs or losses or to some other disadvantage if demands are not met. The greater the costs or disadvantages that an organization can impose, the greater is its power at the bargaining table. For these reasons, this might be called "opponent-pain" power.

Type I bargaining power might also be called "opponent-gain" bargaining power to emphasize the fact that its existence rests upon the ability to grant some gain or advantage to the other party. The fact that we refer to the other party as "opponent" should not obscure the fact, mentioned previously, that there is a community of interest as well as a conflict of interest between the parties in a bargaining situation.

Most current discussions of bargaining power possibilities for agriculture seem to be centered on opponent-pain power. Farm co-operatives have used the first kind for some time. But the gains obtained have not been as many or as large as some farmers think they ought to be able to obtain by bargaining. Although farmers have exercised the first kind for some time, they have by no means exercised opponent-gain power in all the situations in which it could be exercised.

Almost the only way an organization of farmers can make the other party worse off if he does not accept its offer is to impose an economic loss through withholding something—products or purchases—that the other party wants or needs. This is what a labor union does when its members go on strike: it withholds the labor needed to operate a plant or business.

Relation Between the Two Types

How are they related? Let us look at some examples. Large chain stores can bargain strongly with their suppliers over the prices and specificationf of goods purchased. A supplier can gain from an assured nation-wide outlet and may be willing to share this gain with the chain stores in the form of favorable prices. But the stores may be able to obtain added gains by refusing to buy if requested concessions are not made. This is because a supplier losing such a big outlet could be hurt both by losing it and by having to develop new outlets in competition with the chains.

Thus, a chain store might say to the company that produces its overalls: "You do not have any marketing costs. We buy all your overalls. We advertise, transport, store, and sell them for you. In return, we pay you these listed prices for each 100 pairs. Next year, we will buy and market all of your overalls as we have in the past," (opponent-gain power). "In return we expect to get the overalls at 5 cents less per pair than we did this year. If you cannot let us have them at this price, we will buy our overalls elsewhere and you can go find another market. And you know that will cost you a lot of money," (opponent-pain power).

When they go on strike, labor unions force employers to experience losses. Rather than suffer these losses, employers may yield to union demands that they would not consider in the absence of a strike threat. The employer also has this same kind of power. He may say, "If your union agrees to abandon these outmoded and restrictive work rules, I will pay so much more per hour than I am now paying," (opponent-gain bargaining power). "If not, your members will have to strike and lose their pay checks while the strike is on," (opponent-pain bargaining power).

It was previously mentioned that an organization possessing the first type of bargaining power might need the second type in order to be able to obtain any benefits for its members. If an organization has opponent-pain power, has it any need for opponent-gain power? Whether it is necessary or not, it will prove quite useful. Its usefulness will be especially apparent during the first attempts at bargaining.

These first bargaining attempts will likely be especially difficult ones. The representatives of the processing firms will feel put upon and abused. Their lives will have been made difficult by producer strikes and withholding actions. They will feel insulted since some producer representatives will have charged that they are profiteers or monopolists. (Agricultural marketing firms' executives do not consider themselves monopolists or profiteers; data will be presented later that indicate they are generally correct. Even if, or especially if, it were true they would resent being called such names.) They will have to change their whole way of doing business — learn new procedures, new rules — if this agricultural bargaining becomes a reality. They will be out to extract vengeance for past annoyances and injustices and to do their best to make these meetings unsuccessful for the producers.

It seems reasonable that people in such a mood will be less apt to insist on a fight to the finish if the producer representatives start out by saying, "Look now, our members can do this and that. We figure it will save you so many dollars per month if they do. Bargaining with us will *not* be only a process in which you surrender or give up things to us. There are benefits for you as well as disadvantages for you if processors and farmers cooperate."

Opponent-gain power emphasizes the cooperative or common interest aspect of a bargaining situation.

Opponent-pain power emphasizes the conflict of interest.

SUMMARY

1. Bargaining power is the ability to negotiate with influence to bring about a desired change.

2. Bargaining involves a community of interest as well as a conflict of interest.

3. Type I or opponent-gain power emphasizes the community of interest. It represents the ability to do something that will make the other party better off.

4. Type II or opponent-pain power emphasizes the conflict of interest. It represents the ability to do something that will make the other party worse off.

CHAPTER 3

Sources of Bargaining Gains

NO MATTER how much bargaining power an organ-ization has nor how skillfully it negotiates, it will not be able to gain anything for its members unless there are gains to be made some place. Where might these gains come from?

EXERCISE OF TYPE I POWER

One source of bargaining gains lies in the successful use of Type I power. Thus, when the members of a grade A milk producers' association convert from can to bulk milk handling, the saving in hauling and receiving costs can be used to pay higher prices to farmers. Farm supply co-ops save petroleum and feed companies some market-ing costs. In return, these co-ops are able to purchase supplies at a lower price.

Gains obtained by farmers through the exercise of opponent-gain power are relatively painless to the ones granting the gains to farmers. It is the nature of this type of bargaining power that it may be used to make farmers better off without making others worse off. In fact, it may make others better off, too. Gains farmers obtain through the exercise of opponent-pain power are quite different. To the extent that farmers are better off, others are worse off.

Where will the money come from to pay farmers the bargaining gains they may obtain through the use of Type II power? There are several possibilities: present profits of marketing firms, lower prices to other resources used in marketing, more efficient operation of firms to lower their costs, and from consumers through higher prices. Let us look at these one by one.

MARKETING COSTS

Marketing margins are one possible source; perhaps some of the money used to pay for marketing agricultural products can be diverted to the farmer. Marketing margins represent the total spread between prices received by farmers for the farm product and prices paid by consumers for the finished product. In this context, all costs and profits involved in local assembly, processing, packaging, storing, transporting, wholesaling and retailing farm products are included. Marketing margins for several farm products as a percent of the retail value of the finished goods are presented in Table 3.1. The remaining portion of the retail value represents the farmer's share of the consumer's food dollar.

Wide variations exist among the different products. This is a result primarily of the different amounts and types of processing and handling necessary to convert different farm products into the kinds and qualities of products desired by consumers.

Large as some of these marketing margins may appear, we cannot tell how much of the margins may be used to pay higher prices to farmers until we know more about the makeup of these margins.

Tables 3.2 and 3.3 contain more detailed information for selected processing and manufacturing industries. These are combined income and expense statements for all firms in these industries for the year 1957. Table 3.2 covers agricultural processing industries; Table 3.3, presented for comparative purposes, covers nonagricultural industries.

Table 3.1. Marketing Margins for Selected Farm-Food Products as a Percent of Retail Value, 1961

	Percent of Retail Value
Choice beef	44
Choice lamb	52
Pork	47
Fryers	50
Eggs	34
Butter	29
American process cheese	59
Ice cream	73
Evaporated milk	59
Fluid milk	57
White bread, all ingredients	86
White flour	67
Corn flakes	90
All fruits and vegetables	70
Apples	64
Grapefruit	83
Green beans	59
Canned corn	89

Source: *Marketing and Transportation Situation,* MTS-144, USDA Econ. Research Serv. Feb. 1962

Table 3.2. Costs and Returns of Selected Food and Tobacco Processing
Industries as a Percent of Value of Production, 1957

	Meat Packers	Ice Cream and Ices	Fluid Milk	Canned Fruits and Vegetables	Flour and Meal	Cereal Breakfast Foods	Bread and Related Products	Cigarettes
Standard industrial classification	2011	2024	2027	2033	2041	2043	2051	2111
Value of production	100.00	100.00	100.00	100.00	100.00	100.00	100.00	100.00
				(Percent)				
Cost items								
Principal raw materials	77.66	30.58	50.98	25.84	70.41	18.63	24.66	43.02
Supplies and other materials	6.56	25.33	14.00	35.83	9.42	26.88	19.54	10.82
Wages to production workers	8.27	9.74	7.23	13.74	5.22	12.92	17.52	6.68
Salaries and wages to nonproduction workers	2.76	9.42	10.81	3.78	2.11	4.35	16.89	.79
Interest	.25	.25	.25	1.39	.28	.28	.14	.88
Insurance	.10	.35	.27	.31	.17	.11	.44	.04
Rent	.22	.65	.66	.49	.04	.05	.67	.08
Property taxes	.17	.49	.31	.46	.31	.46	.40	.23
Depreciation and depletion	.67	3.54	1.82	2.16	.77	1.17	2.42	.62
Advertising	.63	1.88	1.88	2.63	.65	4.66	2.86	5.18
Contract work	.06	.07	.08	.09	.02	.01	.07	.00
Fuel	.23	.33	.47	.58	.11	.50	.99	.09
Electricity	.19	.96	.52	.30	.53	.40	.47	.12
Miscellaneous expense	1.56	12.93	7.24	9.13	6.85	16.86	8.14	21.28
Net profit before taxes	.67	3.48	3.48	3.27	3.11	12.72	4.79	10.17

Sources: U.S. Bureau of the Census, *Annual Survey of Manufactures; 1957,* U.S. Govt. Print. Off., 1959. U.S. Census of Manufactures, 1958, Vol. I, *Summary Statistics,* U.S. Govt. Print. Off. 1961. U.S. Census of Manufactures, 1958, Vol. II, *Industry Statistics,* Parts 1 and 2, U.S. Govt. Print. Off., 1961. U.S. Internal Revenue Service, *Statistics of Income 1957-58 Corporation Income Tax Returns,* U.S. Govt. Print. Off. 1960. John Sherman Porter, (editor in chief), *Moody's Industrial Manual — American and Foreign, 1960,* Mcody's Investors Service, New York, 1960.

Table 3.3. Costs and Returns of Selected Nonfood Manufacturing Industries as a Percent of Value of Production.

	Thread Mills	Pharmaceutical Preparations	Grease and Tallow	Petroleum Refining	Steel Foundaries	Farm Machinery	Tractors	Motor Vehicles and Parts
Standard industrial classification	2223	2834	2886	2911	3323	3522	3531	3717
Value of production	100.00	100.00	*Percent* 100.00	100.00	100.00	100.00	100.00	100.00
Cost items								
Principal raw materials . . .	60.49	20.80	51.41	67.87	11.08	26.39	26.77	50.78
Supplies and other materials	*	4.59	*	11.68	19.08	26.72	27.10	16.92
Wages to production workers	16.72	10.10	15.68	5.30	34.46	21.32	19.13	12.85
Salaries and wages to nonproduction workers . .	4.94	10.35	6.73	2.08	9.32	9.00	6.53	3.09
Interest	.42	.59	.58	.48	.66	.56	.57	.27
Insurance	.12	.17	.68	.11	.22	.24	.06	.03
Rent	.27	.28	.32	.27	.33	.30	.20	.10
Property taxes	.35	.47	.43	.52	.58	.64	.52	.38
Depreciation and depletion	1.85	1.48	3.08	3.07	2.34	2.21	2.98	1.90
Advertising	1.00	3.57	1.00	.47	.38	1.08	1.09	.87
Contract work	1.45	.56	.18	.11	1.33	.55	.55	.12
Fuel	.76	.29	1.86	1.16	2.07	.60	.61	.39
Electricity	1.05	.33	.85	.49	3.06	.38	.38	.29
Miscellaneous expense . . .	6.80	26.23	15.09	2.15	6.14	4.18	7.60	1.59
Net profit before taxes	3.78	20.19	2.11	4.24	8.95	5.83	5.91	10.42

* Raw materials and supplies are included in the principal raw materials item.
Sources: Same as Table 3.2.

Costs and returns are presented as a percent of value of production. Value of production is the value of sales plus the increase or minus the decrease in the volume of finished and semifinished product in inventory. It also includes receipts for work done for others.

For most of the agricultural industries, cost of principal raw materials is by far the largest component of costs. The major portion of this item constitutes payments to farmers. A sizeable portion of the remainder represents payments to other firms for partially processed farm products. For simplicity we will suppose that all of this item is paid to farmers. The importance of cost of principal raw materials varies widely among the nonfood industries in Table 3.

"Wages to production workers" also includes supplementary employee benefits such as employers' social security contributions and unemployment insurance premiums. These amount to 10 to 15 percent of the total shown. This category is generally smaller in the agricultural than in the nonfood industries. Nonproduction workers include firm officers, supervisory personnel, sales and delivery men and those engaged in advertising, clerical, purchasing, financial and other administrative activities. This item is fairly large in those industries using substantial amounts of delivery labor, such as dairies and bakeries. Except for these industries, this item is generally smaller in the agricultural industries shown than in the nonfood industries shown.

Miscellaneous expenses include such costs as office expenses, research and development expense and consulting services. With the exceptions of meat packing and pharmaceuticals, this item is a relatively large item in the agricultural industries in Table 3.2 compared with the nonfood industries in Table 3.3.

Sources of bargaining gains are not limited to manufacturers of farm products. All marketing agents should be investigated for possible sources. Table 3.4 shows a profit and loss statement of retail chain stores. Goods purchased for resale constitute the major cost item. Payroll expenses account for about half the remainder.

Table 3.4. Costs and Returns as a Percent of Net Sales for 53 Retail Food Chains, 1960

	Average	Net Sales Volume Per Chain ($ million)		
		Less than 20	20 — 100	100 or more
Number of chains	53	18	16	19
Average sales per store (thousands)	1,223	1,180	1,299	1,217
			(Percent)	
Net sales	100.00	100.00	100.00	100.00
Cost of goods purchased for sale	78.38	81.02	79.39	78.21
Supplies	1.07	.98	.90	1.10
Payroll	10.53	7.69	8.79	9.48
Payroll for administrative personnel*	-	1.57	1.47	1.10
Interest	.32	.29	.35	.32
Insurance	.15	.22	.21	.14
Real estate expense	2.05	1.71	1.82	2.08
Taxes other than income	.62	.53	.57	.63
Fixture and equipment expense	1.48	1.25	1.69	1.46
Advertising	2.12	2.52	2.16	2.11
Service purchased	.25	.09	.20	.26
Utility expense	.74	.76	.72	.74
Traveling expense	.10	.11	.10	.09
Miscellaneous expense	.81	.78	.86	.81
Net income before taxes from retailing operations	1.38	.48	.77	1.47
Income before taxes from other sources†	1.36	1.19	1.37	1.37

* Based on 14, 12 and 17 chains, respectively.
† Net profit from real estate operations, interest earned on assets, cash discounts earned, etc.
Source: Wilbur B. England, Operating Results of Food Chains in 1960, Graduate School of Business Administration, Harvard Univ., Bul. 162, Aug., 1961.

Profits

Let us look first at profits as a possible source of bargaining gains. With the exception of cereals and cigarettes, net profits as a percentage of value of production are smaller in the industries in Table 3.2 than in those in Table 3.3.

Suppose the firms in the industries in Table 3.2 had made no profits in 1957 and had paid out this money to farmers in the form of higher prices. Prices received by farmers would have increased by the percentages in Table 3.5. The figure for cereals is the largest. Unfortunately, even if this industry were to greatly increase prices it pays to farmers, total farm income would be little affected since less than 1 percent of our grains is sold to the cereal industry.

The other percentages are of a much smaller magnitude. They would be worth having, of course. But are farmers liable to get them? Certainly farmers are not going to be able to reduce profits to zero. It is doubtful that this is what farmers want to do. Before profits are reduced to zero, firms will raise the prices they charge their customers or reduce prices paid other production inputs. These two are to be taken up later. If profits were reduced to zero and held there, firms would sooner or later cease operating and farmers then would have no place to market their products.

Table 3.6 contains some other data which are relevant here. The farmers' share of the consumers' food dollar has run about 40 percent in recent years. Suppose it is typical for farm products to move to the processor, then to the wholesaler, to the retailer and the consumer. If profits of all agricultural marketing firms had been reduced to zero in 1960, farm prices could have been 15 to 20 percent higher.

It is apparently common practice for large businesses to attempt to carry out their operations so as to earn at least a minimum satisfactory profit rate. Without intensive study of typical firms in various industries it is not possible to say what this rate is. We would probably be not far off to say that the minimum rate is at least as large as the smallest profit rate in Table 3.6. That is

Table 3.5. Percent Increases in Farm Prices, 1957, if Industries in Table 3.2 Had Used All Profits To Pay Higher Prices To Farmers

Industry	Percent
Meat packing	1
Ice cream and ices	11
Fluid milk	7
Canned fruits and vegetables	13
Flour and meal	4
Cereal, breakfast foods	68
Bread and related products	19
Cigarettes	24

Table 3.6. Profits as Percentage of Sales

Year	45 Food Processing Companies		5 Wholesale Food Distributors		8 Retail Food Chains	
	Before taxes	After taxes	Before taxes	After taxes	Before taxes	After taxes
Average 1935–39	3.6	3.0	-	-	1.8	1.5
Average 1947–49	3.9	2.3	2.7	1.7	2.3	1.4
1950	4.6	2.5	2.1	1.2	2.4	1.3
1951	3.6	1.7	2.1	1.1	1.9	.9
1952	3.5	1.6	1.6	.7	1.9	.8
1953	4.0	1.9	2.0	1.0	2.1	1.0
1954	3.8	1.9	1.9	1.0	2.0	1.0
1955	4.4	2.2	1.7	.9	2.1	1.0
1956	4.3	2.2	1.9	1.0	2.4	1.1
1957	4.1	2.1	1.8	.9	2.6	1.2
1958	4.5	2.2	2.3	1.2	2.6	1.2
1959	4.8	2.4	2.1	1.1	2.6	1.2
1960	4.8	2.4	2.3	1.2	2.6	1.2
Average 1947–60	4.2	2.1	2.1	1.2	2.3	1.2

Source: *Marketing and Transportation Situation*, MTS—143, USDA Econ. Research Serv., Oct., 1961, p. 10.

before tax rates of 3.5, 1.6 and 1.9 percent for processors, wholesalers and retailers, respectively. These are not much different from actual rates for 1935 — 39, which was not a particularly prosperous period. The highest actual rates occurred in 1960. If 1960 profit rates had been equal to these minimum satisfactory rates and the remaining profits had been used to pay higher prices to farmers, farm prices could then have been some 5 percent higher. As indicated by Table 3.4, the increase would have been more than this for some commodities, less for others. In other years, the increases in farm prices would have been smaller. In 1952 they would have been zero. From this we see that farmers cannot expect to obtain dramatic gains out of processors' and marketing firms' profits.

This also is the case with labor unions. They do not make appreciable gains for their members at the expense of reduced profits. Reynolds has concluded [1] ". . . it is remarkably difficult for wage-earners to encroach appreciably on business profits."

Wages and Salaries

In Table 3.2 principal raw materials is commonly the largest single item. For firms handling farm products, this represents payments to farmers. In Table 3.4 cost of goods purchased is the largest item. The next largest item is commonly wages and salaries.

A rough idea of what might be available from the wages and salaries can be obtained by supposing that employers had paid employees 10 percent less and used this money to pay higher prices to farmers. Table 3.7 indicates the resulting percentages by which farm prices for various products would have risen. The average would have been 4 percent, with a range of from 1 to 14 percent. Assuming wholesalers and retailers also reduced labor expenses by 10 percent, the average increase in farm prices would have amounted to about 6 percent. Again, as in the case of profits, worthwhile but not dramatic.

---

[1] Lloyd G. Reynolds, *Labor Economics and Labor Relations,* 3rd ed., Prentice-Hall, Englewood Cliffs, N.J., 1959, p. 471.

Table 3.7 Proportion by Which Farm Prices Could Have Been Increased in 1957 if Salaries and Wages Had Been 10 Percent Less, Industries in Table 3.2

Industry	Percent
Meat packers	1
Ice cream and ices	6
Fluid milk	4
Canned fruits and vegetables	7
Flour and meal	1
Cereal, breakfast foods	9
Bread and related products	14
Cigarettes	2
Weighted average	4

As a practical matter, can wage rates and salary rates be cut by 10 percent in order to permit paying higher prices to farmers? It is highly unlikely. Under any conditions, labor unions will fight bitterly to prevent wage rate and salary reductions. They will probably fight even harder if they find that the employers plan to pay them less money so that they can pay farmers more money. It would be only slightly less difficult to cut wages and salaries of nonunion workers. Whether represented by unions or not, employees resent and oppose pay cuts. Pay cuts are liable to cause many of them to join unions. Employers do not like to take steps which will encourage their employees to join unions.

Any gains from this source are most apt to come in the form of future higher prices to farmers at the expense of smaller future wage and salary increases. How rapidly might this work itself out? Since 1950 average hourly earnings of employees of food processing and marketing firms have risen by 10 percent every 2 to 2 1/2 years. [2] Thus, *all* pay increases would have to be stopped for 2 to 2 1/2 years to reduce labor expenses by 10 percent to raise farm prices by 5 to 6 percent. And in this long a time other developments might occur so that what would otherwise be a 5 or 6 percent increase might turn out to be much smaller. If all wage and salary increases cannot be eliminated, but only reduced in amount, several more years would be required.

There is another possible way of reducing labor expenses. This is by operating more efficiently. This will be discussed in more detail a little later.

Other Expenses

After wages and salaries the next largest item of cost is supplies and other raw materials, followed by miscellaneous expenses. The latter covers such a variety of things it is not possible to say anything about it. For the former the conclusion is the same as for wages and salaries. The main gain to farmers would have to come about through smaller future increases in prices paid for

---

[2] *Marketing and Transportation Situation,* MTS—143, USDA Econ. Research Serv., Oct, 1961, P. 6.

these items. This is probably also true for miscellaneous expenses.

There are some cost items which farmers might prefer not to reduce. Advertising, research and development are among these. Many farmers apparently feel we should, if anything, have more rather than less advertising, research and development pertaining to farm products. Depreciation and depletion are cost items whose reduction is liable to lead to less rather than more income for farmers over the long run. The reason is that depreciation and depletion are the main source of funds for new buildings, machinery and equipment. New machinery and equipment normally embody technological improvements which tend to reduce costs of operation. Cutting down on the depreciation and depletion account will force businesses to use older and less efficient equipment for a longer time.

Differences Among Firms

These industry-wide cost and profit data obscure the inter-product and inter-firm variations that exist within an industry. Through bargaining, farmers might be able to obtain higher prices from most firms handling one product while unable to obtain higher prices from firms handling another product within the same industry. Of two firms handling the same product, one may be able to pay higher prices to farmers while the other can not. We turn now to a look at cost variations among businesses handling the same product.

In Table 3.4 we see that retail food chains with larger sales volumes on the average, have a higher net income per sales dollar: they have lower cost per sales dollar.

The relation of cost to size has two aspects; the first relates to capacity, that is the largest possible amount a plant or store can handle. Plants with larger capacities generally have lower costs per unit processed than do smaller plants when both are operated at about the same percent of capacity. A study of poultry slaughterhouses in New York City during 1949—50 revealed considerable

1265495

cost reductions for firms with larger volume.[3]   Firms processing an average of 508,000 pounds of poultry annually had operating costs of 7.7 cents per pound. Processors with an average volume of 861,000 pounds had operating costs of 5.9 cents per pound. Firms processing an average of 2,497,000 pounds of poultry had operating costs of 4.9 cents per pound.

In a study of 26 dairy manufacturing plants in eastern South Dakota in 1957, it was found that the annual average price paid to farmers ranged from 62.9 cents per pound of butterfat for plants receiving less than 250,000 pounds of butterfat to 65.7 cents for plants receiving over one million pounds.[4]

These economies of large scale operation are quite pervasive. They have been found to exist in egg handling, poultry processing, butter making, fluid milk operations, mixed feed manufacturing and vegetable canning plants, to name a few places. Several factors explain the lower unit costs in larger plants. First, workers in larger plants operate equipment of a larger capacity and tend to be idle a smaller portion of the day. Hence, labor require- ments and, therefore labor costs tend to be lower per unit of output in larger firms. Utilities used in processing also tend to be utilized more efficiently in large firms resulting in lower per unit fuel, electricity and water bills. As the size of the plant increases larger buildings and equipment can be employed which are less costly per unit of capacity than those used in smaller firms. Price reductions in the form of quantity discounts for containers and supplies other than raw materials also contribute to lower unit operating costs for large plants.

That gains from economies of large scale operation may be quite sizeable is illustrated by an example of the recent experience of five cooperative creameries in northeast Iowa. These creameries received whole milk,

---

[3] A. J. Ashe, *Operation of Poultry Slaughterhouses in New York City, 1949-50,* Cornell Univ. Agr. Exp. Sta. Bul. 883, 1952.

[4] Ralph E. Nelson and Travis W. Manning, *Procurement Policies and Practices of Dairy Manufacturing Plants in Eastern South Dakota. Part I. Market Structure and Behavior,* S. Dak. Agr. Exp. Sta. Bul. 497, 1961, p. 35.

separated it, sold the skim milk and made butter from the cream. They merged into one organization and replaced the five separate creameries by one larger consolidated plant. The consolidated unit started operaion in April of 1958, at the time dairy support prices were dropped. Cost savings from consolidation permitted the plant to continue paying farmers the same price as before, while other dairy plants in the area reduced their paying prices by 15 to 21 cents per hundredweight of milk. In the first complete year of operation the plant made one million pounds of butter. During this period it was able to pay patrons about 5 cents per pound of fat more than they would have received if the cooperatives had not consolidated. This amounted to $40,000 more income to the farmers.

It is one thing for groups of farmers to merge several cooperatives into one organization and to capitalize on the economies of large scale operation. Here the farmers are actually the owners of the firms. To capitalize on these economies in other cases will require different procedures. They may, for example, bargain with one large plant for a price so favorable that smaller plants with higher costs will be forced to shut down and can be replaced by one large low-cost plant. In other cases, one or more bargaining associations may be able to work with the owners of several small plants to induce them to form a corporation to set up a large plant.

The relation of cost to size has a second aspect. For a plant or store with a given capacity, the closer it can operate to capacity, the lower will be its costs. For example, in a study of whole milk creameries it was found that when they operated at 90 percent of capacity their cost per pound of butter was 7 to 10 percent higher than when operating at capacity. When operating at 70 percent of capacity, their costs per pound of butter were 33 to 41 percent higher.[5]

Some firms are more efficient than others operating under the same set of conditions. The range, in total cost

[5] J. R. Frazer, V. H. Nielsen and G. W. Ladd, *Manufacturing Costs: Whole Milk Creameries,* Iowa Agr. Exp. Sta. Special Rept. 17, 1956, p. 11.

of seven midwestern egg plants during June 1957 was
10.3 to 13.2 cents per dozen for cartoned eggs and 6.9
to 9.9 cents per dozen for loose-pack eggs.[6]   Total
manufacturing costs for five Minnesota spray drying
plants producing between 4 and 5 million pounds of
dry milk annually in 1947 ranged from a low of 4.3 to
a high of 5.1 cents per pound.[7]   The range in operating
costs of five small firms processing poultry in New York
City was found to be 6.5 to 9.8 cents per pound, for
seven medium firms, 4.8 to 7.2 cents, and for seven
large firms, 4.3 to 6.4 cents.[8]   Actual costs also were
gathered from 13 plants manufacturing butter in 1950. [9]
Three of these plants with approximately the same
volume reported manufacturing costs of 4.49, 4.62 and
4.77 cents per pound of butter manufactured.

These variations in costs are relevant to a discussion
of sources of bargaining gains. Some plants may be
induced by bargaining to pay higher prices while other
plants cannot afford to pay them. Plants with lower
costs may already be paying higher prices to farmers.
If they are not, a strong bargaining association may be
able to induce them to pay higher prices and still leave
them better profits than their competitors have.

This will put pressure on competing firms to raise
their prices to farmers. Some firms, for various reasons,
will be unable to do so and will gradually be forced out
of business as farmers shift from them to higher paying
buyers. Others, who have been operating at higher costs
because of lax or incompetent management, will be able
to reduce their costs in order to return higher prices to
farmers. This is similar to what many people have
suggested as one of the main effects of labor unions.
They have argued that since labor unions apparently
increase the cost of labor to businesses, businessmen

---

6 Robert M. Conlogue, *Candling and Cartoning Eggs at Country Plants,*
USDA Marketing Res. Rept. 366, 1959, p. 14.

7 Dale E. Butz and E. Fred Koller, *Costs of Drying Milk in Minnesota
Plants,* Minn. Agr. Exp. Sta. Bul. 413, 1952, p. 16.

8 Ashe, *op. cit.*

9 J. R. Frazer, V. H. Nielsen and J. D. Nord, *The Cost of Manufacturing
Butter. A Study Based on Data from 13 Iowa Creameries,* Iowa Agr. Exp.
Sta. Res. Bul. 389, 1952, p. 32.

have to run the rest of their operations more efficiently.

They have also argued that businessmen try to speed up the rate of technological improvement in order to keep costs from rising as fast as they otherwise would with rising wage rates. This may also be possible in agricultural processing and marketing where firms forced to pay higher prices to farmers will try to offset this by increasing the efficiency of their plant operations.

CONSUMERS [10]

Farmers may be able to obtain bargaining gains from consumers. One way might be to adapt production and marketing practices more completely to existing demand to increase consumer expenditures. This might involve, as an earlier example suggested, adjusting timing of marketings to variations in seasonal demands. It might involve changing production practices to fit more closely with consumers' preferences for various grades and qualities of the product.

Another way to obtain bargaining gains from consumers might be to simply charge higher prices to consumers without making any production or marketing changes to adjust to consumer preferences. Adapting production and marketing patterns to consumer preferences does not have some of the disadvantages of raising prices without making changes to adjust to consumer preferences.

The amount of bargaining gains farmers can obtain by raising prices is restricted by certain characteristics of consumer behavior. Union gains, too, are limited by these same characteristics. One noted observer of labor unions has concluded: [11]

> Management resistance to union demands
> is motivated mainly by doubt that customers
> will pay high enough prices, or will buy enough

---

[10] This discussion of consumers as a source of bargaining gains is quite brief. It primarily consists of certain conclusions about consumer behavior which are needed for an understanding of bargaining. The reader who wants more information to support these conclusions is referred to Appendix A.

[11] Reynolds, *op. cit.*, p. 153.

goods at these prices, to keep the company in profitable operation. The union is not really up against management. It is up against the limitation of consumer demand in the product market, as estimated by and transmitted through management.

The limitation on charging higher prices without making other changes to make products more attractive to consumers is essentially this. In our economy the top limit to farm product prices is determined primarily by the level of consumer income, the size of the population and the volume of farm production. The first two of these cannot be changed much by producer groups and the demand for most farm products is such that a reduction in marketings results in a rise in price and an increase in farm income, whereas an increase in marketings results in a fall in price and in farm income.

Retail Level Demand

To see why this is so, we need to look at characteristics of consumer demand. Beef and pork are important sources of farm income and are typical of all farm products so far as the characteristics of consumer demand for them are concerned. Along the horizontal axis in Figure 3.1 is measured total annual beef consumption. Along the vertical axis is measured the annual average retail price of beef. The solid line through A and B represents the average 1956—1960 relation between price and consumption. The line through A and B in Figure 3.2 presents the same information for pork. (The derivation of these two figures is discussed in Appendix A, Tables A.1 to A.3).

In both figures the lines fall downward to the right. Although both figures are based on data for 1956—1960 only, this falling off to the right is typical of the situation for longer periods of time, too.

The line through A and B in Figure 3.1 can be interpreted in either of two ways. Let us use point A for an example. At this point, price is 81.1 cents per pound and annual consumption is 14.12 billion pounds. (1) Each point on the line shows the highest possible average

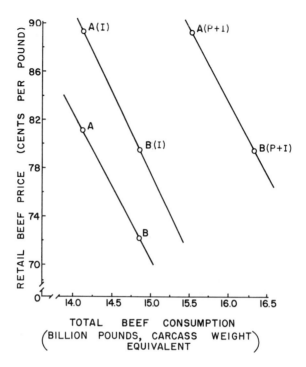

Fig. 3.1—Relation between annual beef consumption and annual average retail beef price, 1956–60. **Source:** Appendix A. Tables A.2 and A.4.

retail price at which the corresponding quantity of beef could be sold annually under average 1956-60 conditions. Point A shows that on the average, 14.12 billion pounds could be sold to consumers annually at a price of 81.1 cents per pound, but not at a higher price. (2) Each point shows the highest level of annual beef consumption which could be achieved at the corresponding price under average 1956—60 conditions. Point A shows that up to 14.12 billion pounds of beef would be purchased annually by consumers at an annual price of 81.1 cents per pound.

The fact that the line in Figures 3.1 and 3.2 slopes downward to the right means that larger volumes of

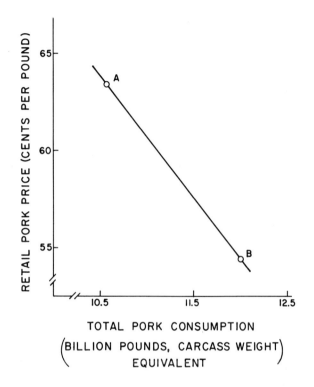

Fig. 3.2 — Relation between annual pork consumption and annual average retail pork price, 1956-60. **Source:** Appendix A, Table A.3.

beef or pork consumption can be attained only by reducing prices under typical conditions.

This tendency whereby price must fall to sell more may be somewhat offset by growth in population and consumer income. Growth in population and consumer income serve to increase demand.

This is illustrated in Figure 3.1. The line through A and B represents the demand relation between beef consumption and beef prices at average 1956—1960 values of population and per capita income. If per capita income had been 10 percent higher than it actually was, the demand relation would have been the line through *A(I)* and *B(I)*. The point *A(I)* corresponds to point *A*. It differs from *A* because of the growth in income (first letter, *I*). The points *B(I)* and *B* are interpreted similarly.

The fact that the line A(I)B(I) is to the right of and above the line AB can be interpreted in either of two ways. (1) At any particular price, total consumption will rise as per capita income rises. For example, at a price of 81.1 cents, a 10 per cent rise in per capita income over average 1956-60 per capita income would increase annual beef consumption from 14.12 billion pounds to about 14.6 billion pounds. (2) Any particular annual volume of beef can be sold at higher prices as per capita income rises. For example, a 10 per cent increase raises the price at which 14.12 billion pounds of beef can be sold annually from 81.1 to 89.2 cents per pound.

If per capita income and population both had been 10 percent higher, the demand relation would have been the line through *A(P+I)* and *B(P+I)*. *A(P+I)* corresponds to *A*. It differs from *A* because of the rise in population (first letter, *P*) and income (first letter, *I*). *B* and *B(P+I)* are similarly interpreted. In other words, when population and per capita income both exceed their average 1956-1960 values by 10 percent, the demand relation for beef will be the line through *A(P+I)* and *B(P+I)*.

Farm Level Demand

Farmers are interested in farm price and farm sales since these are what directly determine farm income. Marketing firms buy from farmers only in order to sell to consumers, either directly or indirectly through other firms. Since farm level demand is derived from consumer demand, we would expect to find the same kind of relation between price received and quantity purchased at the farm level as at the retail level. We do, as can be shown by a number of examples.

The case of turkeys, between 1960 and 1961, furnishes one example. Between 1960 and 1961, live-weight slaughter of turkeys increased from one and a half billion pounds to nearly two billion pounds, an increase of 32 percent. Between 1960 and 1961 the average farm price of turkey fell from 25.3 cents to 18.5 cents, a decrease of 27 percent, and gross income from turkeys fell from $376 million to $363 million. Farm production increased 32 percent, farm price fell 27 percent and farm income dropped. It has been estimated that if 1961 production had equaled 1960 production, farm price would have been nearly 27 cents and gross income to turkey growers would have been nearly $400 million.

Beef and pork furnish several examples. Between the first quarter of 1955 and the first quarter of 1956, farm marketings of beef increased 12 percent. It took a 26 percent decline in farm price of beef to get people to buy 12 percent more beef. During the same period, farm marketings of pork increased 12 percent. It took a 27 percent decline in the farm price of pork to get people to buy 12 percent more pork. Between the first quarter of 1957 and the first quarter of 1958, farm marketings of beef declined 10 percent and the farm price of beef increased 34 percent. During the same period, pork marketings declined 6 percent and pork price at the farm level increased 15 percent. From 1958 to 1959, egg marketings increased 3 percent and price declined 18 percent. Between 1959 and 1960 egg marketings declined 3 percent and price increased 14 percent.

Each of these examples — turkeys, beef, pork and eggs — illustrate the operation of the law of demand. As farm marketings increase, farm price tends to decline; as farm marketings decrease, farm price tends to rise. Since we are here concerned with bargaining power an immediately relevant example is reported by B. I. Freeman, manager of the Great Lakes Cherry Producers Marketing Cooperative.[12]   In 1958 the national cherry crop was 103 thousand tons or 20 percent below average. The association controlled about 40 percent of the tonnage available to commercial processors. The association

---

12 Berkley I. Freeman, "Negotiating a Realistic Price: Our Experience Last Year," *Published in Proceedings of the 4th National Conference on Fruit and Vegetable Bargaining Cooperatives,* Jan. 4, 1960, USDA Farmer Coop. Serv., pp. 16—24.

negotiated a price of $165 a ton, 14 percent above the previous eight year average price. By 1959, the association was stronger. Its membership represented a larger percentage of the total cherry crop; but the total cherry crop was 40 percent greater than 1958 and 11 percent greater than the ten year average. The association was able to obtain a negotiated price of $125 per ton or $40 per ton less than the 1958 price. This, in spite of its increasing membership, and because of the larger total crop.

It is worthwhile, too, to notice some of the things that the association had to do to maintain this $125 price. Two small processors, located in Pennslvania, refused to buy cherries from the association and the association arranged to sell these to larger processors. In Michigan, one large processor returned 400 tons of cherries. The association then had to establish a receiving station to receive these cherries and move them from central Michigan to southern Michigan processors. The association had to undertake the marketing of cherries for a number of its members who had previously sold their cherries to brokers, because the brokers were unable to market the cherries at the negotiated price. In New York, several small processors were unable to finance the purchase and processing of cherries at a price which would cover the negotiated farm price plus the processing costs. The association then had to take over these cherries and contract with processors to pack the cherries at a somewhat lower price and the association had to make up the difference to these members from their assessment and service charges.

At the end of 1959, the association found itself in a position where it had to be very careful in financing its operations because it was still carrying a one-half million dollar inventory of cherries. Thus, between 1958 and 1959, the association grew stronger. It gained members and its membership controlled and produced a larger portion of the total cherry crop. In 1959, it had to work hard and make special arrangements to handle some of the cherry crop. It ended up 1959 with a large inventory of cherries and still its negotiated price was

$40 below the negotiated price of the previous year. It is no accident that this drop in price came at the same time as a 40 percent increase in total farm production of cherries. It is simply the operation of the law of demand. Since agricultural processing firms purchase from farmers in anticipation of selling to consumers, the prices that they pay to farmers and the volumes that they buy from farmers are affected by what they believe consumers will be willing to pay for the quantity and quality of product offered to them. That is, the demand for beef cattle or hogs or eggs or fresh cherries from the farmer is a derived demand. It derives from consumer demand for the products which are made from the cow or the hog or the egg or the fresh cherries.

We can use the line through *A* and *B* in Figure 3.1 to show how farm level demand is derived from consumer demand. The process is presented in detail in Appendix A, Table A.4. During the period 1956 to 1960, farm price of beef averaged about 60 percent of the retail price of beef. Thus, the retail price of 81.1 cents, point *A* in Figure 3.1, was split 81.1 x 0.60 = 48.7 cents to the farmer and the rest, 32.4 cents, to processing and marketing firms. From this we get the point *AF* in Figure 3.3 (*F* for farm).

Together points *A* and *AF* tell this story. At a retail price of 81.1 cents per pound, consumers would buy 14.12 billion pounds of beef. Since farm price is 60 percent of retail price, processors will pay 48.7 cents per pound for this much beef. Points *B* and *BF* say: To sell 14.85 billion pounds, retail price can be no higher than about 72.2 cents. With this retail price, farm price will be 43.3 cents (72.2 x 0.60 = 43.3).

The distance between the two lines *AB* and *AFBF* in Figure 3.3 represents marketing margin. The earlier discussion of marketing firms as a source of bargaining gains can also be looked at from the standpoint of this graph. The line *AFBF* represents farm level demand when marketing charges run 40 percent of retail cost. Suppose marketing charges could be cut to 30 percent of the retail price; farm price would then be 70 percent

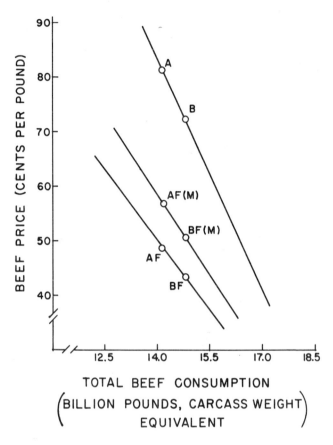

Fig. 3.3—Relation between total beef consumption and farm and retail beef prices. **Source:** Appendix A, Table A.5.

of retail price. Farm level demand would then be represented by the line through *AF(M)* and *BF(M)*. The *M* (for marketing charges) means these points differ from *AF* and *BF* because of the change in marketing costs. Thus, we see that reducing marketing costs permits farmers to receive higher prices for the same amount of output. By contrast, if marketing costs do not change, charging higher prices means that less will be sold. This, remember, is the meaning of the fact that the demand curve slopes downward to the right.

Conversely, if marketing charges should rise above 40 percent of the retail price, farm level demand would be represented by a line below *AF* and *BF*.

Reductions in marketing costs, remember, can be achieved by cutting profits of marketing firms, reducing wages and salaries paid by such firms, lowering prices marketing firms pay for other production inputs, or increasing efficiency of marketing firms by improved management or improved technology.

A useful device for measuring the relation between price and quantity purchased is elasticity of demand. It measures the percentage change in quantity resulting from a 1 percent change in price, provided income and population do not change. Table 3.8 presents elasticities of demand at the farm level. The figure 0.68 for cattle means that a 1 percent rise or fall in the farm price of cattle results in a 0.68 percent fall or rise, respectively, in the number of cattle that dealers will want to buy from farmers. The number 1.08 for calves means that a 1 percent rise or fall in the farm price of calves results in a 1.08 percent fall or rise, respectively, in the number of calves buyers will want to purchase from farmers. The quantity taken always moves in the opposite direction from price. Elasticity of demand indicates the proportional change in quantity buyers will want to purchase resulting from a one percent change in price.

Elasticity of expenditure, which is one minus the elasticity of demand, indicates what happens to total expenditures (total farm receipts) when price varies. The figure 0.32 for cattle means that a 1 percent rise or fall in farm cattle price results in a 0.32 percent rise or fall in farm income from the sale of cattle. The figure - 0.08 for calves means that a 1 percent rise or fall in the farm price of cattle results in a 0.08 percent fall or rise in farm income from sale of cattle. When elasticity of demand is less than one (as it is for most farm commodities) any increase in farm price serves to increase farm income. So long as marketing charges, population and income are unchanged, farm price can be increased only if less is sold by farmers. Hence, for most farm

Table 3.8. Elasticity of Farm Level Demand and Farm Level Expenditure for Farm Products Used for Domestic and Export Consumption, 1955—57

Farm Product	Elasticity of Demand	Elasticity of Expenditure
Cattle	0.68	.32
Calves	1.08	-.08
Hogs	0.46	.54
Sheep and lambs	1.78	-.78
Chickens	0.74	.26
Turkeys	.92	.08
Eggs	.23	.77
Milk used for:		
Fluid milk and cream	.14	.86
Evaporated and condensed milk	.26	.74
Cheese	.54	.46
Ice cream	.11	.89
Butter	.66	.34
Soybean oil *	4.00	-3.00
Cottonseed oil *	6.92	-5.92
Other food oils *	7.04	-6.04
Lard, total use *	.54	.46
Vegetables	.10	.90
Sugar *	.18	.82
Potatoes and sweet potatoes	.11	.89
Wheat [†]	.02	.98
Rough rice [†]	.04	.96
Rye [†]	.04	.96
Corn [†]	.03	.97
Barley	.07	.93
Oats [†]	.01	.99

* Wholesale price and quantity demanded.
† Not including demand for export or for feed.
Source: George E. Brandow, *Interrelations Among Demands for Farm Products and Implications for Control of Market Supply,* Pennsylvania Agr. Exp. Sta. Bul. 680, 1961, p. 59.

products, reducing output raises price and raises farm income.

Table 3.8 indicates that the opportunity for financing bargaining gains to farmers by charging higher prices to consumers varies among commodities. Increasing farm prices of calves, sheep and lambs, soybean oil, cottonseed oil and other food oils reduces farm sales enough to reduce farm income, as indicated by their negative elasticities of expenditure. Increasing farm prices of turkeys by 10 percent will reduce turkey sales by 9.2 percent and increase turkey farmers' income by only 0.8 percent. Increasing farm prices of vegetables by 10 percent, on the other hand, will reduce farm sales by only 1 percent and will raise vegetable growers' income by 9 percent. The smaller the elasticity of demand, the less will be the proportional reduction in farm sales resulting from a farm price rise and the greater will be the proportional increase in farm income.

Effect of 1950—1960 Increases in Income, Population and Marketing Charges

As Figure 3.3 indicates, reducing marketing costs has the same effect on farm level demand as does growth in population and consumer income. Each permits the same amount to be sold at higher prices or else permits more to be sold at the same price.

Between 1950 and 1960 both retail prices and consumer purchases of livestock and livestock products rose, but farm prices fell. The ideas presented in previous sections can be used to show why this happened.

For most livestock products, annual consumption equals annual farm production. Since 1950 population and per capita income have risen at a rate that would have permitted retail prices for livestock and livestock products to rise 6 to 7 percent per year if consumption and farm production had remained constant. These rates of population and income growth would have permitted consumption and farm production to rise about 2.5 percent per year with no decline in retail prices. During this period output of livestock and livestock products rose somewhat less than 2.5 percent per year. Hence retail prices rose somewhat.

But marketing charges rose, too. The farmer's share of the consumer's dollar fell faster than retail prices rose. Hence farm prices fell. (This is discussed in more detail in Appendix A, Figures A.4, A.5 and A.6.)

Effect of Substitute Products

The availability of substitute products also places an economic limit on bargaining power. As used here the term substitute means one product which can be used to replace another. It carries no connotation of inferiority. In this sense, butter and margarine are substitutes for each other; beef and pork are substitutes for each other. An all-inclusive organization of beef producers, for instance, would find its ability to get higher beef prices limited by prices and supplies of pork, poultry, cheese, fish and eggs. That is to say, the demand for beef depends on the prices of beef and on the prices of various substitute products, that is, products which consumers can use in place of beef to serve the same or similar purposes so far as nutritional value, tastes and method of preparation are concerned. For example, Table 3.8 shows the price elasticity of demand for cattle to be 0.68. Remember, this means a price increase of 1 percent will reduce purchases by nearly seven-tenths of 1 percent and a price decrease of 1 percent will increase purchases by nearly seven-tenths of 1 percent.

Increasing the price of cattle will influence the purchase of other farm products, also. A 1 percent increase in the price of cattle, which will reduce the number of cattle purchased by seven-tenths of 1 percent, will increase the number of calves purchased by a quarter of 1 percent, increase the number of hogs purchased by one-tenth of 1 percent and increase the number of sheep and lambs purchased by nearly one-half of 1 percent. Thus, we see that the existence of related or substitute products also comes into the picture. If beef producers, for example, are successful in forming a large and strong association and succeed in raising the farm price of beef, they will also succeed in partially displacing beef consumption by consumption of other meat products, dairy products, poultry and sea foods. The greater their success in raising prices, the more beef will be displaced by other products.

The existence of substitute products is one reason why increases in retail price reduce consumption. When the retail price of pork rises, for example, people reduce their consumption of pork. They can adjust for this by increasing their consumption of substitute products — beef and broilers, especially.

As Kenneth Naden, of the National Council of Farmer Cooperatives, has put it: "A strike to achieve higher prices by hog producers, for example, would result in nothing but an accumulation of fat hogs and an immediate switch by consumers to beef, chicken, turkey, fish and other substitute products."[13]

Farmers are not the only ones whose operations are affected by the existence of substitutes. Prior to World War II, Aluminum Company of America had a monopoly on the virgin aluminum market in this country. However, the prices which it could set for virgin aluminum were limited by the fact that virgin aluminum could be replaced by scrap aluminum, by imports of aluminum, and also in some cases by other metals.

The relation of virgin aluminum to other metals was somewhat like the relation of a two-row to a four-row corn planter. A four-row corn planter is generally faster and more efficient in planting corn on large, relatively level farms. But if two-row corn planter prices remained constant while four-row corn planter prices rose, they could get so high that people could not afford to use them. In other words, the price of four-row corn planters could get so high relative to the two-row that the total cost of operation would be less by using the less efficient two-row corn planter. That was the case with aluminum. Virgin aluminum was preferred for many uses, but if its price became too high, other metals could be substituted.

The limitations existing because of substitutes also show up in labor markets. Every once in a while we

---

[13] "Who Will Do Your Bargaining?" *Better Farming Methods,* 33:18, Oct., 1961.

read in the newspaper about a jurisdictional strike or a jurisdictional dispute between two unions. Some of these jurisdictional disputes arise because there are two different products which can perform similar functions and one product is handled by members of one union while the other is handled by members of another union.

The amount that can be gained by bargaining for higher prices is limited by the law of demand and the existence of substitute products. The law of demand tells us that charging higher prices for a product will reduce sales of that product unless population and consumer income grow fast enough to increase demand sufficiently to offset the reduction in purchases. Part of consumers' response to the higher price will consist in a shift to substitute products.

SUMMARY

1. One possible source of bargaining gains lies in the exercise of opponent-gain power.

2. Gains may be obtained by reducing marketing costs. The possibilities include reduced profits to marketing firms, reduced wages and salaries to employees, reductions in prices paid other inputs by marketing firms and increased efficiency of marketing firms.

3. On the average, possible gains from these sources are relatively small. Some individual firms, however, might be the source of sizeable gains.

4. Consumers are a potential source of bargaining gains.

5. If product quality or pattern of marketings is improved simultaneously with charging consumers higher prices, everyone can gain.

6. Charging consumers higher prices, without doing anything to improve product, usually reduces the level of consumption.

CHAPTER 4

Relation Between Bargaining Power and Supply Control Power

INDIVIDUAL PRODUCTS

SOME ECONOMISTS have equated bargaining power with monopoly power, where monopoly power means ability to control supply. One reason is that a person or organization who controls the supply of a product — who has a monopoly on the product — also has a monopoly on opponent-gain or opponent-pain power as related to that product. Thus, when Aluminum Company of America had its monopoly on virgin aluminum, it was the only organization that could grant Type I gains that involved the use of aluminum. Likewise it was the only organization that could impose Type II bargaining losses by withholding aluminum.

A more important reason why they equate bargaining power to monopoly power is suggested by the discussion of demand. A smaller volume of output can be sold for a higher price than a larger volume of output. Thus, a farm organization that could control production to meet demand at satisfactory prices could enhance the income of producers, whether it had bargaining power or not. If production cannot be controlled, the possible gains from bargaining power are much more limited.

Average annual beef consumption in 1956 to 1960 was 14.3 billion pounds. The line $AF\ BF$ in Figure 3.3 indicates this could have been sold for 47.5 cents per pound of carcass-weight equivalent on the average. If production had been 13.3 billion pounds, farm price could have averaged 55.5 cents.

Turkeys furnish another example. In 1961, nearly two billion pounds of turkeys were marketed for a per capita supply of 10.7 pounds. The result was an average farm price of 18.5 cents and a gross income from turkeys of $363 million. If farmers had marketed one and a half billion pounds for a per capita supply of 8.0 pounds, average farm price would have been nearly 27 cents and gross farm income would have been $400 million.[1]

Thus, an organization that had the authority to restrict beef or turkey production could limit production to obtain higher prices for its members whether it had bargaining power or not. This is also true of other farm products.

The level of production of farm products is determined by the individual decisions of thousands of farmers operating independently. (For some products their freedom of choice is, of course, restricted by government programs.) One factor influencing farmers' decisions is the relative profitability of various products. As one product becomes more profitable, future output of that product is stimulated.

Turkeys furnish one example of the relation of level of output to profitability. In 1960, the farm price of turkeys averaged a little over 25 cents per pound. Gross income from turkeys was about $376 million and net profit from growing turkeys was in the neighborhood of $70 to $80 million, with a cost per pound of around 18 to 21 cents per pound. In other words, net profits were roughly one-fourth of total gross income from turkeys. A profitable year for turkeys.

1961 was nearly as unprofitable as 1960 was

---

[1] George W. Ladd: "How Many Turkeys Should We Produce?" *Turkey World,* 37 (May, 1962): 16-17.

profitable. 1961 production exceeded 1960 production by nearly 32 percent. The high profit from turkeys in 1960 attracted increased production in 1961. We recently made a survey of some 345 turkey producers in Iowa and obtained information on their 1960 and 1961 production. Of these growers, 31, or nearly 10 percent, had produced no turkeys in 1960 and did produce turkeys in 1961. There were only 12 producers who produced turkeys in 1960 and did not produce in 1961. Of the total of 345 turkey growers, only 70 reduced production from 1960 to 1961 and 275 increased production between the two years. These growers increased their total production of turkeys from 3.5 to 4.5 million turkeys between these two years. 1960, a highly profitable year for turkey growers, was followed by a large increase in production. Due to the operation of the law of demand, this increase in output depressed farm prices and 1961 was an unprofitable year for turkey growers.

The 1962 turkey crop was 15 percent smaller than the 1961 turkey crop. An unprofitable year in 1961 was followed by a reduction of turkey supply in 1962.

Farm production of hogs provides another example of the response of future supply to current profitability. The annual pig crop of one year is affected by the hog-corn price ratio during the previous year. This ratio is computed by dividing the average price of 100 pounds of live hog by the price of one bushel of corn. It shows how many bushels of corn 100 pounds of live hog will buy. Feed is an important part of the total cost of hog production; amounting to 65 to 70 percent of total cost. Corn is the main feed and prices of other feeds are closely related to corn prices. Thus, the hog-corn price ratio is a measure of the profitability of hog production. As this ratio rises, hog production becomes more profitable and farmers raise more hogs. As this ratio falls, hog production becomes less profitable, and farmers raise fewer hogs.

This relation in which increased profitability results in increased output has been observed for most farm products of importance to Midwest farmers: eggs, wheat, corn, beef, milk and cream in addition to turkeys and hogs. It has also been observed for cotton and tobacco among others.

One way of increasing the profitability of hog production is to raise the price of hogs while the price of corn remains the same. The effect of raising the price of hogs will be to reduce purchases of hogs and increase production. We can use Figure 4.1 to show this.

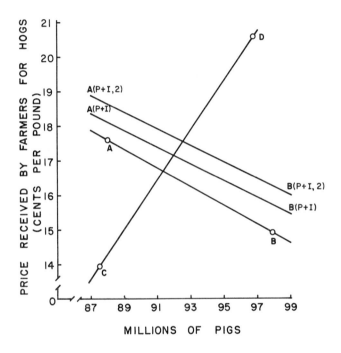

Fig. 4.1 — Hog demand and supply. **Source:** Appendix A, Table A.3 and Appendix B, Table B.1.

The line in Figure 3.2 represents the average relation between annual pork consumption and retail pork price in 1956-1960. Line *AB* in Figure 4.1 represents the average relation between annual hog production and annual average hog price of the same year. (The way it is derived from Figure 3.2 is presented in the Appendix, Tables A.3 and B.1.) Line *AB* in Figure 4.1 shows the maximum average price at which each annual pig crop could have been sold. Alternatively it represents at each price the largest pig crop that could have been sold.

Line *CD* shows the average 1955-1961 relation between average hog price one year and the size of next year's pig crop. (The way it is obtained is shown in Appendix B.) This line shows that a high hog price one year is followed by a large pig crop the next year and a low hog price is followed by a smaller pig crop.

Lines *AB* and *CD* intersect at a price of $16.70 and a volume of 91.4 million pigs. These are almost equal to the average price and average production of the period 1955-1961, being only 2.3 and 1.2 percent too low respectively.

Line *A(P+I) B(P+I)* represents farm level demand following one year during which population and per capita income grow at their annual average rate. The line *A(P+I,2) B(P+I,2)* represents farm level demand after two years of average growth in population and per capita income.

Suppose that during one year an association of hog producers negotiates an average farm price of $17.50. (See Table 4.1.) Line *AB* shows processors will buy 88.4 million pigs from farmers that year. The line *CD* shows that a farm price of $17.50 one year will be followed the next year by hog production of 92.5 million pigs. Suppose that between this year and the next year population rises, but per capita income falls so that total demand remains the same. In the second year processors will buy only 88.4 million pigs at a price of $17.50. This will leave 4.1 million pigs which farmers raise in the second year, but cannot sell. (If farmers are to sell all the pigs they produce, farm price must fall to $16.40.)

If production remains the same for two more years while population and income grow at their average rates, there will be less surplus the third year and price will rise slightly above $17.50 in the fourth year. To maintain the price of $17.50, the association will have had to purchase 6.0 million pigs over a two year period.

Table 4.1. Effect Over Time of High Negotiated Price on Production, Purchases and Price

Income and Population Values	Year			
	1	2	3	4
	1956-60 Average	1956-60 Average	1956-60 Average Plus 1 Year's Growth	1956-60 Average Plus 2 Year's Growth
Supply line	C-D	C-D	C-D	C-D
Demand line	A-B	A-B	$A(P+I)-B(P+I)$	$A(P+I,2)-B(P+I,2)$
Farm price	$17.50	$17.50	$17.50	$17.60
Production		92.5	92.5	92.5
Purchases	88.4	88.4	90.6	92.8
Surplus		4.1	1.9	
Price at which total output can be sold		$16.40	$17.05	$17.60

This illustrates the most serious problem an associ-ation will face if it is successful in raising prices through its bargaining activities. If it increases prices faster than the growth in demand warrants, it will be faced with a situation in which members cannot sell all they produce. Large volumes of unsold products will put downward pressure on prices and it will be impossible to maintain prices at the negotiated level.

In order to protect the price it will become necessary either to (a) buy up the surplus and dispose of it in new markets that are noncompetitive with present markets or else (b) impose production controls on the members in order to guarantee that total production will not exceed the amount that can be sold at the negotiated price. The first alternative is not available to most im-portant agricultural products. The organization, there-fore, will have to find some equitable and acceptable scheme for dividing the available market among the members.

Such interference with their operations will drive some members out of the organization; it will create problems in member and nonmember relations. The higher prices will presumably go to nonmembers as well as to members. The nonmembers, too, will want to increase production. If nonmembers can increase their production at the same time members cannot expand and may even be cutting back production, it is question-able how many members will stay members. In these conditions many members will face powerful temptation to drop out and let the organization make the market while they enjoy the high negotiated price without suffer-ing the nuisance of limitations on output.

The turkey example shows that present producers are not the only ones who must be considered, either. Ten percent of the farmers surveyed had not produced turkeys in 1960 but did produce turkeys in 1961. High prices not only stimulate output from present producers, they also encourage new producers to enter the market. What do members gain if they support an organization's efforts to obtain higher prices if they then have to cut back their production to make room for the increased output of present nonmember producers and the output of new producers? About all the members have succeeded in doing is to make a market for other producers.

The magnitude of the problem of lost sales resulting from higher prices will vary among commodities. If the demand line through A and B in Figure 4.1 were nearly vertical, sales would be reduced little by raising price from $16.70 to $17.50. The surplus in Table 4.1 would then be smaller. Commodities whose demand elasticities (Table 3.8) are near zero will suffer relatively small losses of sales from price increases. The problem of lost sales resulting from higher prices will tend to be less serious for these commodities than for the commodities with larger elasticities of demand.

We will return to this point later in discussing some of the problems organizations face in building and retaining bargaining strength.

Labor unions have long been aware of the fact that wage rates are influenced by the supply of labor, i.e., by the amount of competition for available jobs. Recognizing this, they have taken steps to reduce the labor supply. Their main efforts have been aimed at reducing the total volume of labor available by legislative means. Unions have supported immigration laws that restricted the inflow of labor from other countries, pension plans which remove older workers from the job market by encouraging their earlier retirement, vacation and holiday plans which reduce hours worked per year per person, and a shorter work week to reduce the number of hours worked per person per year. Unions have supported legislation, notably the Fair Labor Standards Act and similar state legislation, which places restrictions on work by women and young people. Some of these, of course, unions support for humanitarian reasons as well as for economic reasons.

In moonlighting, a worker holds down a second job in addition to his regular position. Moonlighting serves to increase the supply of available man-hours of labor. Unions discourage moonlighting by their members.

Some unions have also attempted to reduce the supply of labor to particular crafts or industries. A few craft unions have established apprenticeship systems which restrict the number of young people that may enter the craft. Some unions (and some professions) restrict entrance through state licensing regulations.

TOTAL FARM OUTPUT

So far we have been looking at one product at a time and it has been amply demonstrated by many studies that raising the price of one farm product relative to the price of other farm products results in increased output of the one with the higher price. What happens if all farm product prices are raised at the same time?

It is possible that this will ultimately result in less farm production as farmers become able to earn more income with the same or less production. If this is so, higher prices for all farm products will reduce production and reduce the magnitude of farm surpluses.

What is there to say about this view? It is possible that it would happen, but there is no historical evidence that it has happened. Historically, higher prices have tended to induce greater output. Some evidence is presented in Figures 4.2, 4.3 and 4.4.

Figure 4.2 illustrates the influence of the parity ratio on total farm output between 1950 and 1957. The parity ratio measures the power of products farmers sell to purchase items they buy. It is the ratio of prices received by farmers to prices paid by farmers. It is one measure of the profitability of farm production just as the hog-corn price ratio is a measure of profitability of hog production. Total farm output is measured by an index of farm output.

In Figure 4.2 the index of farm output and the parity ratio are measured as changes from year to year. Each point represents the change in the parity ratio during one year and the change in farm output the following year. The interpretation of this figure will become clearer after an examination of some specific

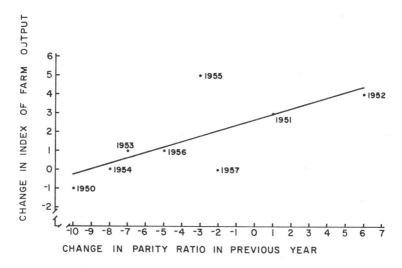

Fig. 4.2—Supply of total farm output. **Sources:** Index of farm output from Econ. Research Serv., **Changes in Farm Production and Efficiency,** USDA Stat. Bul. 233, 1961. Parity ratio from Office of Business Economics, **Business Statistics, 1961,** A Supplement to the Survey of Current Business, U.S. Dept. Comm., 1961.

points in the graph. From 1948 to 1949 the parity ratio fell 10 points; from 1949 to 1950 the index of farm output fell 1 point. This is represented by the point labeled 1950. Between 1949 and 1950 the parity ratio rose 1 point; farm output rose 3 index points between 1950 and 1951. The point labeled 1951 represents this situation. The other points can be similarly interpreted. If we draw in lines connecting the points for successive years we note that all of them slope up to the right except the line connecting 1956 and 1957. The line actually drawn in Figure 4.2 represents the line of average relationship. This indicates that, normally, high prices for farm products tend to bring forth larger output in future years and low prices tend to depress output. High prices stimulate output more than low prices depress it, as seen in Table 4.2. The two years in which the parity ratio rose were followed by years of increased output. Three of the six years in which parity ratio fell

Table 4.2. Number of Years In Which Parity Ratio and Total Farm Output Moved In Indicated Directions.

Parity Ratio	Total Farm Output			
	Rose	No Change	Fell	Total
Rose	2	0	0	2
Fell	3	2	1	6
Total	5	2	1	8

were followed by a rise in output. Figure 4.2 does show, however, that large price declines depress output more than small price declines, but not much more.

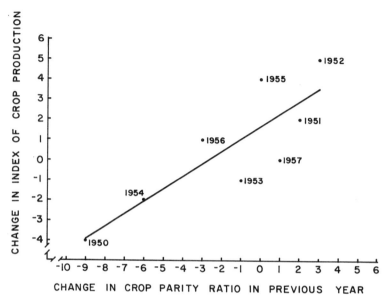

Fig. 4.3 — Crop supply. **Sources:** Index of crop output from Econ. Research Serv., **Changes in Farm Production and Efficiency,** USDA Stat. Bul. 233, 1961. Parity ratio from Office of Business Economics, **Business Statistics, 1961,** A Supplement to the Survey of Current Business, U.S. Dept. Comm., 1961.

Whereas Figure 4.2 relates to total farm output, Figure 4.3 refers to crop production. The crop parity ratio is the index of prices received for farm crops divided by the index of prices paid by farmers. Here again, output and parity ratio are measured as year-to-year differences. All lines which might be drawn in to connect successive years slope upward to the right except the line connecting 1956 and 1957. The line actually drawn, which is the line of average relationship, also slopes up to the right. The slope upward to the right shows that high prices received in one year tend to stimulate crop production the next year and low prices received tend to depress future production.

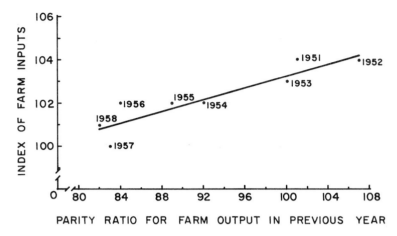

Fig. 4.4—Demand for inputs. **Sources:** Index of inputs from Econ. Research Serv., **Changes in Farm Production and Efficiency,** USDA Stat. Bul. 233, 1961. Parity ratio from Office of Business Economics, **Business Statistics, 1961,** A Supplement to the Survey of Current Business, U.S. Dept. Comm., 1961.

The same story is also told by Figure 4.4, which shows how the parity ratio one year affects the volume of productive inputs used the next year. Productive inputs are such things as seed, feed, fertilizer, gasoline, land, and man-hours of work. All are items needed to produce crops or livestock. The use of more inputs represents an effort to produce more output. The line of average relationship in Figure 4.4 slopes upward to the right. This shows again how high selling prices serve to stimulate output and low selling prices to depress it.

The output-stimulating effect of high selling prices has been observed over long periods of time. During 1920-57, an increase of 10 percent in the ratio of prices received to prices paid by farmers resulted in a subsequent 1 to 2 percent increase in total farm output. During 1911-58, an increase of 10 percent in the ratio of prices received for crops to prices paid resulted in a subsequent 1.5 to 2.5 percent increase in crop output.

[65]

During 1911-58, an increase of 10 percent in the ratio of prices received for livestock and livestock products to prices paid by farmers resulted in a subsequent increase in output of livestock and livestock products of about 5 percent.[2]

It is, of course, possible that farm prices have never risen sufficiently high to reach this critical point where further price increases would result in reduced output. This raises three considerations:

1. Evidently farm prices are not now at a sufficiently high level that price increases will serve to reduce output. As prices rise they will for sometime (until they reach this critical level) induce increases in farm output. Further, price increases above this level will then be necessary to bring output back down to its present level.

2. How high, then, must prices go above their present level to reach this critical level?

3. Will the public accept farm prices this high? This is relevant, since the public will not stand for prices which they believe to be unfairly high.

Suppose that this critical price, above which further price increases will reduce output, is not unfairly high in the public's mind. And suppose it is reached. Now this whole argument, that higher prices will reduce output, emphasizes the "work" or hours of farm family labor side of the output question. Is it necessary that increased output require more work by the farmer and his family? To put it another way: Is it necessary that fewer hours of hard work means less production?

Maybe there is a relation and maybe not. Almost every farmer can think of ways he could maintain his level of production with less work *if* he had the money or credit to buy the labor-saving machinery and equipment needed or *if* he had the money to employ more hired labor. It is possible that, when prices have reached the critical level, farmers' incomes will be sufficiently high that they can afford to buy (with their own or borrowed money) this machinery and equipment or to hire ad-

[2] Zvi Griliches: "Estimates of the Aggregate U.S. Farm Supply Function," *Jour. Farm Econ.* 42:282-93, 1960.

ditional labor. Then farm production will remain constant or may even rise, even though farm families are working no harder than before.

It is possible that this critical price does not exist at all. In this case, farm prices will never rise high enough to reduce output.

There are essentially three ways of increasing the profitability of a particular product or of all farm products. One is to raise the price received for the product, e.g., the price of hogs; another is to reduce prices paid for items used in producing the product, e.g., the price of corn; a third way is to reduce production costs by adopting improved managerial practices or production techniques. The first two methods are appropriate objectives of bargaining; the latter is not an objective for bargaining. (Of course weather also affects profitability.)

One important ingredient of costs of livestock production is feed. In the Midwest the ratio of feed costs to total costs ranges from one-third and up for dairying to one-half for eggs to 65 to 70 percent for hogs and beef cattle. Reducing prices paid by farmers for feed means little to the operator who raises his own feed and feeds all he raises. It means lower prices received by those farmers who sell feed or feed ingredients.

To increase profitability by reducing prices paid by farmers, they would look primarily to agricultural machinery, petroleum, fertilizer and other farm supplies. As indicated by Table 2.3, even the complete elimination of manufacturers' profits in the tractor, farm machinery and petroleum refining industries would not reduce prices farmers pay for these items by more than around 5 percent. Since complete elimination of profits is not likely, significant reductions in prices paid by farmers will have to come about through lower wages and salaries or through lower prices paid by these industries to their suppliers. The gains via this route are apt to be fairly small and to cumulate slowly.

SUMMARY

1. Higher farm prices for individual agricultural products increase their volume of production in the future.

2. Historically, higher prices for all farm products have tended to increase total farm output. We can expect this to be true in the future, at least until prices received by farmers become substantially higher than they are now.

3. The fact that high price tends to depress consumption and to stimulate production creates a serious problem for any bargaining association that succeeds in substantially raising farm prices. Members will want to produce more than they are able to sell at the negotiated prices.

CHAPTER 5

Other
Organizational
Activities

UP TO NOW, when the word bargaining has been used, it has usually meant bargaining over price. There are, of course, various prices which may be the subject of bargaining. Bargaining may involve the average price — the price level. It is likely also to involve price differentials: seasonal, grade or quality, weight, volume or geographic price differentials.

As far as grade or quality is concerned, the selection of grading standards is an appropriate topic for bargaining. Method of farm-to-plant delivery may be a topic for bargaining. This might cover the kind of carton or pack to use (in the case of fruits or vegetables), whether the farmer of the plant should perform hauling, or the time of day or week for delivery.

A good example of a nonprice bargaining activity which a farm organization might perform is furnished by recent developments in the marketing of grade A milk. Under pressure from labor unions many bottling plants have moved to 4-day or 5-day bottling. As a result, extreme day-to-day variations exist in milk requirements of bottlers. This creates problems for dairy farmers who must furnish additional storage facilities to hold them over the long weekend or who must divert part of their milk to lower valued manufactured milk uses.

Here is a case in which the bargaining power of unions has forced a change in operations onto bottlers and created additional costs for dairy farmers. Preventing this additional cost from falling on the farmers would be a suitable activity for a farm bargaining organization. There are various ways this might be done. One would be to assure that the various bottlers stagger their bottling week so that the day-to-day requirements would be more stable. Another would be to require bottlers to construct additional milk storage facilities. Exactly what might be done would vary depending upon the local milk sanitation laws.

Nor should it be overlooked that there are many activities besides bargaining that an organization of farmers may undertake to benefit its members. One type is common in dairying: cooperative processing and marketing facilities. Another activity frequently undertaken by cooperatives is quality improvement: helping members to maintain or to improve the quality of their product. Associations of farmers frequently participate in advertising, promotional or educational efforts to improve the demand for their product.

Associations may perform orderly marketing functions. These involve sending various qualities, sizes or colors to the markets where they will bring the greatest returns; controlling the weekly flow of marketings to prevent alternate market gluts and shortages; and controlling seasonal marketings to take advantage of seasonal variations in consumer demand.

Some associations supply market news to their members which they can use in planning and organizing their activities: information on current price, production and market conditions; outlook information; and information on Washington developments in agricultural policy.

Nonbargaining activities may furnish a basis for Type I bargaining power. Nonbargaining activities may contribute to bargaining power.

CHAPTER 6

Organizational
Conditions[1]

AN ORGANIZATION possesses opponent-pain bargaining power if it is able to make its opponent worse off if he refuses the organization's offer. To use opponent-pain bargaining power successfully, a farm group or organization must meet a number of conditions. Each condition not fully met lessens its ability to impose economic pressure on the other party and may also lessen its ability to exercise opponent-gain power.

CONTROL OF VOLUME

Condition 1 is that the organization must control something that the other party wants or needs to obtain from the members of the organization. This means that an organization of producers must represent a sufficient

[1] The discussion here and in the following chapter on Obstacles to Attaining Unity is drawn mainly from the following references: Dorwin Cartwright and Alvin Zander (eds.), *Group Dynamics Research and Theory,* 2nd. ed., Row, Peterson and Co., Evanston, Ill., 1960; George Caspar Homans, *Social Behavior Its Elementary Forms* Harcourt, Brace and World, Inc., New York, 1961; George W. Ladd and J. Robert Strain "What About Bargaining Power for Farmers?" *Iowa Farm Science,* 16:3-5, 1961; and James G. March and Herbert A. Simon, *Organizations,* John Wiley and Sons, Inc., New York, 1958.

volume of the product before it can be effective. Meeting this condition appears more difficult for farmers selling corn or hogs or other products raised in nearly every state, than for farmers selling specialized products, such as cranberries or bing cherries, grown in a relatively few local areas.

After four years of effort to establish a bargaining cooperative among Eastern apple producers, Carroll R. Miller of the Appalachian Apple Service reported:[2]

A final problem is that we have six states to deal with in trying to coordinate our activities. There are great distances between them. Varieties are different. Buying methods are different. There are also complexes of inferiority and superiority — big states and little states and this doesn't encourage cooperation.

The more of the total volume controlled by an organization, the greater is its bargaining power. Its bargaining power decreases as the proportion of the total volume controlled by its members becomes smaller. The other party can then turn more easily to other sources. If these are adequate and readily available, the organization may have practically no power in bargaining.

The relevance of this condition can be illustrated by the history of grade A milk bargaining associations. Historically, each metropolitan fluid milk market tended to be isolated from other fluid milk markets and each one had its own milk shed. This isolation existed mainly because of the lack of economical refrigerated transportation facilities. A bargaining association consisting of all producers supplying a particular market then controlled all of the existing supply. Bottlers either bargained with and reached agreement with the association for their milk, or they did not obtain milk.

Nowadays fluid milk can be easily transported long distances in refrigerated tank trucks. Bottlers can more easily turn to alternative and more distant sources of

[2] Carroll R. Miller, "Problems Involved in Establishing a Bargaining Cooperative Among Eastern Apple Producers," *Proceedings of the 3rd National Conference on Fruit and Vegetable Bargaining Cooperatives,* Jan. 10-11, 1959, USDA Farmer Coop Serv., p. 22.

supply. Therefore the local association has less power than formerly. To meet this problem, some local associations occasionally have made agreements with other associations representing the same product. Several grade A milk bargaining associations from different markets will agree that no other member will negotiate with or supply a prospective buyer while the buyer is negotiating with the member of the group that normally supplies him. In this way each association, in effect, obtains control over a larger portion of the total supply.

But even the organization of all producers of a product into one association does not in itself assure bargaining power. The amount of bargaining power depends also on how well the organization meets several other conditions. As a matter of fact, an organization that cannot meet these other conditions probably will not be able to satisfy this first condition. The fact that an organization has all producers as members does not assure that it will be able to maintain high prices through the exercise of bargaining power. As shown in the last chapter, to maintain continued high prices it will be necessary for the organization to restrict production and marketings of its members. That is, it is not enough simply to have all growers as members; it may also be necessary to restrict the volume marketed by members.

As the turkey example of the preceding chapter illustrates, and as you know from experience, when production of one product becomes sufficiently profitable, farmers who had not been raising the product will start raising it. Hence, even after an organization obtains control of current supply, to maintain control it will be necessary to get these new producers into the organization.

UNITY

The position taken in negotiations by the representatives of a bargaining organization usually represents a compromise among the different positions preferred by various groups of members. The final agreement, in turn, will represent a compromise between this compromise position and the position of the bargaining opponent. It will not be the agreement every member wanted.

Each member must be willing to allow the organization to make some decisions on behalf of himself and all other members. Each member must further be willing to support each decision even though it may not be the one he would have preferred. These decisions may pertain to prices; quality, seasonal or quantity price differentials; time and method of delivery; or marketing restrictions. The need for unity will be most strongly felt, and the ability to maintain unity will be most severely tested, during those periods when an organization must curtail the production of its members in order to maintain high prices for their products.

Kenneth Naden of the National Council of Farmer Cooperatives points out this need for unity and for group decisions in a discussion of bargaining power for farmers when he writes: "The cardinal principle is group action by farmers — the acceptable way in a democratic free enterprise society — many individual farmers acting with unity of purpose and with central decision-making."[3]

Condition 2, then, is that the organization must have cohesion and disciplinary power over its members. Members must have a unity of purpose and must be willing to make the sacrifices necessary to achieve the advantages of a strong bargaining position. They must delegate to the organization some of their rights as individuals and must be bound as individuals to the decisions that are made by their organization.

Members of a labor union allow their negotiation representatives to bargain for minimum acceptable wage rates, fringe benefits and working conditions. If a majority of the members vote to strike, however, all must strike — even though some members might be willing to work for less or would rather not strike and lose their pay. If a substantial number agreed to work for less than the union demands and went back to work after

---

[3] "Agriculture Can Compete With Big Business," *Better Farming Methods,* 32:16, Dec., 1960.

the majority had voted to strike, the union would not have much success as a bargaining agent.

Craft unions operated successfully in this country long before industrial unions did. There are a number of reasons. They all spell unity.

A craft union [4]

> . . . . is an association of employees bound together by common employment, skill and interest in a relatively narrow occupation or group of closely related occupations. The particular craft or calling, being based upon the attainment of a relatively high degree of skill after a rather prolonged period of training, usually is made up of the upper grades of the working class . . . .

Examples of craft unions are the Brotherhood of Railroad Signalmen of America and the International Brotherhood of Bookbinders. There are also amalgamated craft unions. These consist of members of two or more crafts performing similar work. An example is the Amalgamated Association of Street, Electric Railway and Motor Coach Employees of America.

An industrial union " . . . is an association composed of all the workers in a given industry, regardless of craft, occupation or degree of skill."[5] Most of the members are unskilled or semiskilled. Examples are the United Automobile Workers and the Textile Workers Union.

In 1932 there were 155 national labor unions with slightly over three million members. Of these unions, 80 percent, containing 85 percent of the members, were craft or amalgamated craft unions. The skilled craftsmen have always had a superior economic and social status in the working world. They have a tradition, which dates back to the medieval guilds, of brotherhood and cooperation in time of trouble. Members of a particular craft have a greater community of interest than laborers in general. They do the same kind of work and expect to

---

[4]Carroll R. Daugherty, *Labor Problems in American Industry,* The Riverside Press, Cambridge, Mass., 1933, p. 418.

[5]*Ibid.,* p. 419.

continue doing so. Attachment to a particular occupation is not nearly so strong among semiskilled and unskilled workers as among skilled workers. There is less turnover among skilled workers; it is easier to maintain unity when there is little membership turnover. During the early years of this country's history, the separate crafts were more homogeneous with respect to nation of origin. Status, tradition, occupation and national origin gave these unions a cohesion and unity which industrial unions did not have. Hence, most successful unions were craft unions.

Many early labor groups did not meet this second condition and failed when some members made separate deals with employers on their own. Early grade A milk bargaining associations had this trouble, too. Processors were able to make separate deals with individual members for lower prices than were negotiated by the association. In some cases, a few members were offered higher prices than the association was attempting to gain for all members. Either of these tactics, when successful, destroys the membership's unity of purpose and also reduces the proportion of the supply represented by the association.

Alan Jensen, manager of the California Tomato Growers Association, in explaining why they failed in their bargaining attempts in 1959 after succeeding in 1958, reported as one reason: " . . . we lacked unity of our growers as expressed through their lack of desire to benefit from the fruits of cooperative action."[6] They failed because they lacked unity. He also reported, "Having been successful in 1958, growers generally felt that we had a powerful organization and each one of them might capitalize to their own benefit." Many members felt that the organization had demonstrated its strength. Accordingly they decided they could do better for themselves if they let the organization set the market and made special deals of their own. We see that success

[6] Alan C. Jensen, " Negotiating A Realistic Price: Our Experience Last Year," *Proceedings of the 4th National Conference on Fruit and Vegetable Bargaining Cooperatives,* Jan. 4, 1960, USDA Farmer Coop. Serv., p. 24.

does not guarantee unity. Success does, however, make it easier to achieve unity.

An informed membership is necessary to obtain unity and strength. Jensen lists lack of communication and lack of information as another reason why they failed in 1959.[7]   Ralph Bunje, general manager of the California Peach Canning Association, emphasizes that the members of the bargaining associations must be well advised and fully informed:[8]

"Bargaining associations and their members need to be *fully informed*. A well informed membership will back up the management and Board of Directors in connection with their bargaining techniques and their bargaining operations, but if the membership is not well advised and not fully informed, then when the crisis stages arrive, there will be no support from the member- ship which is so important."

Members need general information on such general topics as current market and demand conditions and production costs. They need a clear understanding of what the organization is trying to accomplish, in the way of prices or differentials or marketing contracts, for example. They need a clear understanding of what they, as individuals, can do to help accomplish these objectives and of how their actions may cause the organ- ization to fail or to succeed.

Disciplinary power over individual members is important, too. An organization cannot long be successful if individual members can, with impunity, refuse to abide by the contract signed by the association whenever it is in their individual interests not to abide by it. Some members will refuse unless they fear the punishment which will follow their violation of the contract.

There is one thing that virtually all large successful voluntary organizations have in common. There are many things the organizations can do to promote their

---

[7] *Ibid*, p. 26 .

[8] Ralph B. Bunje, "Improving the Climate for Price Negotiation," *Proceedings of the 4th National Conference on Fruit and Vegetable Bargain- ing Cooperatives,* Jan. 4, 1960, USDA Farmer Coop. Serv., p. 29.

members' welfare. Labor unions not only try to improve their members economic welfare by getting higher wage rates, unemployment benefits and the like for them; unions try to improve their members' working conditions, the speed with which they must work and their schedules of work. They push for adequate safeguards from injury in hazardous jobs. Unions try to obtain seniority provisions in contracts to protect older and more experienced workers who have "more right" to their jobs than do younger workers with less time on the job. They push for better medical care for on-the-job injuries and expanded medical benefits for emplousss' families. Unions not only work for a better deal for members from employers; they also support legislation to improve conditions for their members.

One reason why unions, as well as other large successful organizations, attempt to do many things for their members is this: Success requires unity. The more an organization can do for its members, the more reasons the members have for supporting the organization. The members will feel more unity, more esprit *de corps,* if their organization is working for them on many fronts than if it is working for them on only one front.

RECOGNITION

The third condition that must be met if power is to be used in bargaining is that the other party must recognize a group's ability to exercise opponent-pain power. To gain such recognition, a bargaining association may have to demonstrate this ability at an early stage of its development. Early union sit-down strikes and producer-group withholding actions are examples of attempts to demonstrate possession of this ability.

It is at this early stage of development that an organization is least apt to possess unity and cohesion. It is also at this early stage of development that members may be least able to stand sacrifices required while imposing losses on the other party. Unions, for example, now use their treasuries to pay strike benefits to their members during a strike. Unions were vulnerable before they built up their treasuries, since members lacked means of support during prolonged strikes.

A strike or withholding action that fails may do serious harm to the organization. It will make it more difficult to obtain cohesion and unity of membership in the future. Many individuals will withdraw their support from an organization that fails. After all, why support an organization that fails to do what you wanted it to do? This in turn reduces the proportion of supply controlled by the group.

PAYING THE PRICE

Condition 4, then, is that the members must be able and willing to bear the cost of withholding their products or purchases from the firm they wish to influence. A hog-withholding action, as an example, has little chance for success unless a large number of producers can afford to hold their hogs while foregoing income from hog sales and experiencing the additional costs of holding and feeding their hogs longer. Producers of some fresh vegetables could lose an entire year's income during a relatively short attempt to withhold their product to get higher prices. Milk producers have a perishable product that must be marketed or dumped. Wheat producers have a product that can be withheld almost indefinitely without a severe loss in quality.

With only one important exception, periods of growing labor union membership in this country have been periods of prosperity and rising employment. During recession and depression union membership has declined. As a matter of fact, until after the Civil War, each depression in this country almost wiped out labor unions completely. One reason is financial. During depression the large number of unemployed cannot afford to pay union dues. Jobs are scarce; until recently wage rates fell during depression. Faced with the prospect of losing his job or taking a pay cut on the one hand and un-employment on the other, the individual's struggle to support himself and his family becomes more important than maintaining a strong union. When the choice is between union support and family survival, union support is sacrificed. During prosperity, on the other hand, a worker can afford to support his family and the union too.

One reason craft unions were successful before industrial unions is financial. The higher wages of craft union members makes it easier for them to afford to support a union. They also suffer less from unemployment.

One reason for the cyclical growth of unions relates to unity, rather than to financial strength as such. During prosperity employers are faced with a strong, profitable market. During recession and depression, sales volume and profit are smaller; businesses may be operating at a loss. If they are closed down by a strike, the amount of profit they lose is much greater during prosperity. Hence, during prosperity they are more anxious to avoid a strike. They are also better able to afford to pay higher wages and fringe benefits. Under these conditions, a union is much more apt to be successful. The very fact of success can attract additional membership and satisfy present members. It is easier to maintain membership unity under these conditions than when employers are unable to increase wages and strikes are failures.

SUMMARY

1. In order to possess power, a bargaining association must meet certain conditions. It must:
   a. Control sufficient volume of product
   b. Possess unity and cohesion
   c. Be recognized
   d. Have members willing and able to pay the price of exercising power.

2. The attainment of (a) will be difficult for many products which are important sources of farm income. Even having all present producers in the organization may not be enough since present producers may increase

their production unless they are restricted, and new producers may enter the business.

3. Attainment of (b) will be difficult for an organization that attempts to limit production by its members.

Obstacles To Attaining Unity

CONFLICT BETWEEN SIZE AND UNITY

THE NEED for satisfying the joint requirements of unity and size presents an organization with a dilemma. Ability to impose opponent-pain power rises as the proportion of supply under control of the association rises. This means larger membership. But larger membership makes it more difficult to achieve unity and cohesion. The source of strength is also a source of weakness.

The reasons for this paradox are not difficult to see. The larger group tends to have a more heterogeneous membership. In a farm organization, the heterogeneity has various aspects:

1. High-volume, low-cost producers and low-volume, high-cost producers. A selling price which is quite profitable for the low-cost producers may not be high enough to permit other producers to break even.

2. Different combinations of enterprises. A hog producer who also raises beef may be willing to see high hog prices cut pork consumption since beef sales will then rise and he may expand his beef operation. A hog

and dairy farmer will be less willing to see high hog prices cut pork consumption since high pork prices will not raise dairy products consumption and his dairy business will not be benefited.

3. Different product qualities. Producers of meat-type hogs will favor one system of hog price differentials. Other producers will favor other differentials. Different producers will prefer different seasonal price differentials.

4. Attitudes toward governmental activity. Attitudes range all the way from strong proponents of laissez faire free markets to adherents of high rigid price supports and strict supply control.

5. Geographic location. Farmers at different locations will prefer different transportation differentials.

6. Age of operator. Young operators still paying for land and machinery are liable to have different attitudes than older established farmers whose land and machinery are paid for.

There will be other sources of differences, too. The point is that larger membership is apt to mean more extreme differences among the members. These will contribute to divergences in the goals members desire the organization to strive for and differences in the way members want the organization to go about achieving its goals. The less uniformity there is in the opinions of the group members, the less cohesion the group has. The less the uniformity the greater the proportion of members who will be dissatisfied with any agreement the organization reaches. A large proportion of dissatisfied members means an organization lacking in cohesion and unity.

This heterogeneity of membership is one reason durable large organizations are those which operate on several different fronts to benefit their members. By working to attain several different goals they are able to satisfy the desires of more than one group of members.

Size enters in another way, also. The strength of support each member gives an organization is affected by the amount he feels he participates in organizational decision-making and the amount of influence he feels he exerts on decisions reached. As the member's felt participation and felt influence decrease, the strength of his support decreases. Both the amount of felt participation and the amount of felt influence tend to be less as membership increases.

The amount of support each member gives an organization is affected by the clarity of his understanding of what the organization is trying to accomplish, how it is trying to accomplish it, his own contribution to the attainment of the goals and the reasons why. A larger membership makes communication among members and between leaders and members more difficult. It therefore reduces the likelihood that each member will be supplied the necessary information to help him understand what the organization is doing and what he can do to help it. Whereas the opportunity for communication declines as membership grows, the need for communication grows as membership grows. The reason is that the greater diversity of membership results in compromise agreements which are satisfactory to fewer people. If members are to support these compromises they must understand them, the reasons for them and the alternatives to them.

After an organization has negotiated an agreement, there will be some members who have incentive to violate the agreement or to withdraw from membership. There will be those members who are dissatisfied with the agreement and who believe they could do just as well for themselves. There will be those members who are satisfied with the agreement, but who are lured away by tempting individual offers from firms attempting to break up the organization. There will be those members who are satisfied with the agreement, but who become disillusioned when they learn of nonmembers who are doing just as well as they are. There will be members who are frightened by threats from buyers to stop buying from them if they remain members or if they abide by the contract.

Suppose we look at an organization with a few members which has reached a bargaining agreement.

There will be some members who will have an incentive to violate the agreement. What will these members do? It depends on just how few the members are. They may be so few that each member knows that if any other member violates the agreement it will operate to his own disadvantage. Then he will retaliate if any other member violates. He will likewise know that if he violates the agreement it will adversely affect the operations of other members. They will then retaliate to bring him back in line. This knowledge that violation will bring punishment will serve to keep each member in line, even though he may be unhappy with some aspects of the agreement. The situation is illustrated in Table 7.1, which shows what happens when three firms reach an agreement and then one violates the agreement. The second column in the table shows the quantity each would prefer to sell. The third column shows the amount each would sell if each abided by the negotiated agreement. Since the agreement is quite unfavorable to C, suppose he violates it. The last column shows the amount each sells then. C's sales rise by 27 percent, whereas A's sales fall by 11 percent and B's by 7 percent. Sales declines of these sizes will evoke retaliatory action from A and B to bring their sales back up.

Table 7.2 divides this market with a total sales volume of 6 million units among 300 firms, rather than among 3 firms. Suppose here again one firm (C) violates the agreement in such a way as to increase his sales by 27 percent (from 15 to 19 thousand). The 4,000 units of sales lost will be divided up among the other 299 firms. Suppose sales are divided up as shown in the last column. The biggest losses in sales are experienced by the D sellers. Each of their losses amounts to only 20 units or slightly over one-tenth of 1 percent. This is so small each firm will probably never even notice the loss. If it does it will figure the loss is too small to worry about.

In the situation in Table 7.1, both A and B are hurt. Each knows he is hurt and wants to retaliate. Each

Table 7.1. Effect When One Member of a Small Organization Violates an Agreement

Seller	Quantity Seller To Sell	Negotiated Quantity To Be Sold	Quantity Actually Sold
A	2	2.3	2.05
B	2	2.2	2.05
C	2	1.5	1.9
Total	6	6	6
	(millions)	(millions)	(millions)

Table 7.2. Effect When One Member of a Large Organization Violates an Agreement

Seller	Number of Each Type of Seller	Quantity Seller Prefers to Sell	Negotiated Quantity to be Sold	Quantity Actually Sold
A	100	20,000	23,000	22,990
B	100	20,000	22,000	21,990
C	1	20,000	15,000	19,000
D	99	20,000	15,000	14,980
		6 million	6 million	6 million

knows the other is hurt and wants to retaliate. Each will retaliate. In the second situation most firms will not even know they are hurt by D's action. Many who realize that they are will decide the loss is too small to worry about. Those few who would like to retaliate will probably not, since they do not know that the others will.

The example illustrates a point that is generally valid. When membership is small, even the member who is disadvantaged by the agreement will abide by it because other individual members will punish him if he does not. When membership is large, he can be fairly certain that other individual members will not punish him and so he might as well go ahead and violate the agreement.

Well, why not solve this by giving the organization the authority to punish members who are violators? This is what is sometimes done. But then this raises further questions. Potential violators will then refuse to join or will withdraw from membership before violating the contract. Further, granting the organization the right to punish erring members is a result of cohesion and unity, not a cause of it. Individual members are not going to vote an organization the authority to punish violators, knowing that the authority can be used on them, unless they are sure they want to support the organization.

In the example with only three sellers, it was pointed out that both A and B would want to retaliate because each was hurt individually. There is another possible reason why each would want to punish C: C is hurting the organization. In groups in which membership is complementary, the actions one member takes in support of the group increase the likelihood that every other member will be benefited by the organization. Further, the ability of each individual to benefit from the organization is increased to the extent that other members support the organization. Membership in a complementary organization with a small number of members, imparts to each member a feeling of responsibility and willingness to devote energy to the group task, as he can see how the success of the organization and the welfare of the other members are dependent upon him. In large organizations individual members lack this feeling of responsibility. The individual does not see how he, as one person, can have any effect on the strength of the organization.

INTERDEPENDENCE OF SUPPORT

Each member who has an incentive to violate an agreement or to withdraw from membership, has it independently of the incentive any other individual may have to do the same. As a matter of fact, the strength of his incentive to violate or to withdraw is apt to be strengthened by the knowledge that others have similar incentives; since there may be some advantage in being among the first to do either of these. The strength of his incentive is certainly not lessened by the knowledge that others have similar incentives.

Contrast this with those people who are definitely satisfied with the agreement and who would like to see it work. The strength of their incentive to abide by it is dependent upon their belief that others will abide by it. Those who are favorably treated by an agreement will in actuality be favorably treated only if the great majority of members live up to the agreement.

Here is the contrast. The strength of each member's incentive to abide by the agreement is dependent upon his conviction that virtually all members will abide by it. The knowledge that some members have incentives to violate the agreement weakens the strength of his own incentive to support the organization and abide by the agreement. The strength of each member's incentive to violate the agreement or to withdraw from membership is either independent of or is actually strengthened by his knowledge that others have these incentives.

There will be people who are neither strongly for nor against the agreement. Knowing that virtually unanimous support from the membership is necessary for success and that some members have an incentive to violate, they are liable to be tipped from indifference to opposition to the organization.

Past success may be one cause of current organizational success. The fact that an organization has been successful in the past is no guarantee of present success, however.

The experience of the California Tomato Growers Association, reported in the earlier discussion of Unity, furnishes an example of one danger which faces an organization once it has been successful. [1] Individual members come to feel that the organization will take care of them; they do not need to take care of the organization. They will let the organization bargain and set price; then they will make special deals on their own. When this happens everyone soon finds out that the organization no longer has the strength to bargain and the individual is not making the special deal he looked forward to. He is selling the same way he did before the organization was formed. Spasmodic or intermittent support is not enough; an organization needs the continuous support of its members.

The number of members in this association of tomato growers is small compared to the number of members it would take to make a successful association in hogs, beef, corn, wheat, manufacturing milk and other widely grown commodities. Maintaining support of the members would be even harder in these larger associations.

RESTRICTIONS ON MEMBERS' PRODUCTION

In Chapter 4, another serious problem facing a successful bargaining association was discussed. That was the problem of restricting output when high selling prices have been negotiated. Restricting output creates friction among the membership since different members will prefer different ways of dividing up the available market. It reduces member's independence of action. Both of these tend to reduce organizational unity. It

---

1 Jensen, *op. cit.,* p. 24.

creates problems in relations between members and non-members. It may result in making a market for non-members at the expense of the members.

There are only two sure ways for a large organization to overcome such divisive forces which will cause its disintegration. One is for the members to possess such an esprit de corps that each finds it repugnant to violate the agreement or to withdraw, i.e., to improve his own finances at the expense of weakening the organization, and for each member to know that he and all others have this same spirit of loyalty and unity. This happy state of affairs is easier to attain in small than in large organizations, in homogeneous than in heterogeneous groups. One reason we had many successful craft unions in this country long before we had successful industrial unions is the smaller size and more homogeneous membership of craft unions.

A second way to overcome this tendency to disintegration is to obtain appropriate legislation. This will be discussed in the next chapter.

SUMMARY

1. To be successful, an organization must be large and united. There is a conflict between the two; as size increases, unity becomes more difficult to attain.

2. The main reasons are the great heterogeneity of membership, difficulties of communication among members and between members and officers, lack of felt participation in decision-making by most members, and lack of feeling of responsibility for and contribution to the large organization.

3. Members who desire to support an organization are vulnerable to the acts of those who have no incentive to support it. Those who have no incentive to support it are not similarly vulnerable to the acts of others.

4. The severest test of unity will come when an association has to limit the production of its members. Few voluntary organizations are strong enough to survive this test.

Role of
Legislation

LABOR UNIONS [1]

LABOR UNIONS are frequently pointed out as the pattern that farmers should follow in forming bargaining associations to raise the prices they receive. Farmers can learn a good deal from the experiences of labor unions.

We earlier discussed the relation between total union membership and volume of employment or unemployment. Figure 8.1 shows total union membership and Figure 8.2 shows union membership as a percent of the employed labor force. They show the periods of rapid growth in union membership to have been prosperity

---

[1] This discussion is summarized from the following: Irving Bernstein, *The New Deal Collective Bargaining Policy,* Univ. of Calif. Press, Berkeley, 1950; Carroll R. Daugherty, *Labor Problems in American Industry,* The Riverside Press, Cambridge, Mass., 1933; Harold W. Metz and Meyer Jacobstein, *A National Labor Policy.* The Brookings Institution, Washington, D.C., 1947; Lloyd G. Reynolds, *Labor Economics and Labor Relations,* (Third ed.), Ptentice Hall, Inc., Englewood Cliffs, N.J., 1959; Russell A. Smith, *Labor Law, Statutory Appendix,* Bobbs-Merrill Co., Inc., Indianapolis, 1953.

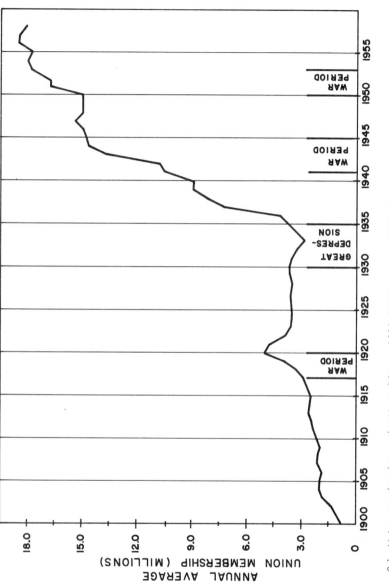

Fig. 8.1.— Union membership in the Untied States, 1900-1958. **Sources:** 1900-1947 membership from U.S. Dept. of Labor, Bur. of Labor Stat., **Handbook of Labor Statistics**, Bul. 916, 1947 ed. p. 130. 1948-58 data from U.S. Bur. of Census. **Statistical Abstract of the United States,** 1958 ed. p. 236 1960 ed. p. 233.

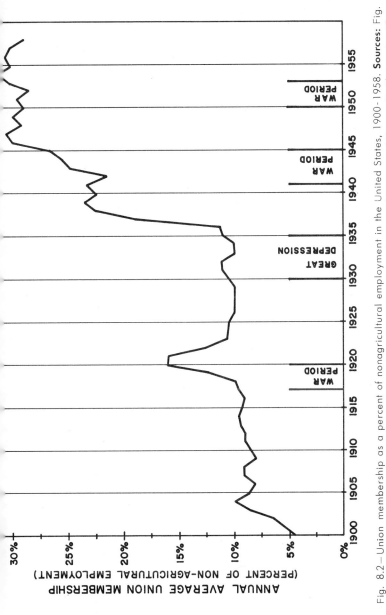

Fig. 8.2.– Union membership as a percent of nonagricultural employment in the United States, 1900-1958. **Sources:** Fig. 8.1 for union membership. Nonagricultural employment for 1900-1954 from Neal Potter and Francis T. Christy Jr., "Employment and Output in the Natural Resource Industries, 1870-1955," pp. 121-122. Published in **Output, Input and Productivity Measurement,** Princeton Univ. Press, Princeton, N.J., 1961. 1955-58 data from Office of Bus. Econ. U.S. Dept. Comm. **Business Statistics A Supplement to the Survey of Current Business,** 1961.

periods: 1900-1904, 1916-1920, 1936-1947, 1950-1957. The period of most dramatic growth was 1933-1947.

In 1920, after 130 years of union activity in this country, union membership reached 5 million: 16 percent of the employed labor force. By 1933 it was down to 3 million and 10 percent of the employed labor force. At this point it began a dramatic growth as shown in Figures 8.1 and 8.2. Part of this growth is due to the fact that the period of 1933 to 1947 was one of almost continuous economic expansion except for a brief recession in 1937-38.

We had fairly long periods of prosperity before in which unions grew—1863-1873, 1897-1904, 1906-1920—but not at this rate. To explain the rate and duration of this growth, we must look to a new force which came on the scene in the early 1930's: legislation which stimulated union growth.

The Situation in 1930

One important way this legislation stimulated union growth was by making illegal many of the means used by employers to combat unions. Among the weapons available to employers in 1930 to combat unions were the injunction, black-listing, the yellow dog contract, industrial espionage and strikebreaking.

The injunction or restraining order was widely used as a device for controlling union activities. The injunction was initially a court order designed to prevent threatened damages to property before they occurred under those conditions in which later action would not provide adequate remedy. It was argued that a strike was certain to injure the employer's justifiable expectation of profit from the continuous operation of his business. By treating this as a form of intangible property, it could be held that any strike was injurious to property. This argument was accepted in many courts. Even where it was not accepted the court might be convinced there was a probability of physical damage to property.

Briefly, the injunction procedure operated as follows. The company would go to a judge and present written complaints that the union was threatening damage to the employer's property. The judge might then issue a temporary injunction immediately. If he did decide to take evidence from the union, the union was restricted in the evidence it could present. Then the judge decided whether to issue a temporary injunction. The injunction was usually drawn in broad terms, restraining anyone from interfering with the employer's business in any way. Anyone supporting the strike in any way might be guilty of a violation. There was a final stage of the procedure at which witnesses were heard and the temporary injunction was either removed or made permanent. This procedure frequently took several months and the strike was lost in the meantime.

A broadly written injunction restraining anyone from interfering with the employee's business in any way, effectively prevented unions from imposing losses on employers during stalemate. Even when narrowly written or laxly enforced they tended to favor employers and weaken the ability of the union to exercise opponent-pain power. They stigmatized the union before the public, demoralized the strikers, interfered with picketing and cost the union time and money for legal expenses.

Judges differed greatly in their use of the injunction decree. On the whole, however, unions regarded it as the employers' strongest weapon.

Another practice widely used from the 1880's on was black-listing. Groups of employers maintained lists of men of known union sympathies and refused to hire such men. Employers also made considerable use of yellow dog contracts under which an employee agreed not to become a member of a union while employed by the company. Then any union organizer attempting to solicit members was inducing workers to break their contract. Inducement to breach of contract was sufficient grounds for obtaining an injunction.

Another common tactic of employers was industrial espionage: placing spies and saboteurs in the union to obtain names of members, to discredit leadership and to weaken the union. "Spy reports were useful through-out the campaign against the union: in forming the blacklist, in discrimination [against union members] and discharge [of union members], in breaking strikes, in initiating the company union [union run by the em-ployer], and in supplying affidavits for an injunction."[2]

Strikebreaking involved a multi-pronged attack upon unions. New workers were hired to replace strikers. Armed guards were hired to protect these new workers and guard property. These armed guards were often deputized. Industrial spies spread dissension and de-featism within the union.

Industrial espionage and strikebreaking were so frequently employed on such a wide scale that some people made a business out of supplying spies and strikebreakers to employers who wanted them.

Other antiunion tactics included firing, demoting, cutting the pay or assigning to less favorable work any worker who joined a union, promising special privileges for not joining a union and hiring strong-arm men to beat up union members or organizers. If the workers did succeed in forming a union the employer could refuse to deal with it and force workers to strike for union recognition.

It is in the early stages of its development that a union is most vulnerable and least apt to win a strike. One important reason is financial; the union probably does not have a treasury to pay strike benefits and the members therefore have no money coming in to tide them over. Another reason is because they lack an *esprit de corps*; each member is apt to be uncertain about how long other members can or will hold out. The reasons for this were discussed under *Obstacles To Attaining Unity*. This makes it more difficult to maintain a strong united front against the antiunion tactics of the employer.

All of these conditions clearly hampered unions in their conduct of strikes and in their attempts to organize.

---

[2] Bernstein, *op. cit.,* p. 10. Brackets enclose explanatory material inserted by me. G. W. L.

They made it difficult or impossible for a union to exercise opponent-pain power or to attain significant size or to attain unity. Tactics similar to these may be directed toward farmers' bargaining associations in efforts to break them up.

Labor Legislation of the 1930's

Legal conditions affecting labor unions underwent a virtual revolution in the 1930's. Legislation enacted during these years played a vital role in bringing about the tremendous growth in union membership since that time.

The first change was represented by the Norris-LaGuardia Act of 1932. It specified yellow dog contracts to be unenforceable in any federal court. It severely restricted the use of the injunction device in labor disputes. It made it much more difficult for an employer to secure an injunction. In addition, it specifically listed several activities which could not be restrained by injunction. Among them were: (a) ceasing or refusing to work, (b) payment of strike benefits, (c) publicizing a labor dispute by any method not involving fraud or violence, (d) peaceably urging others to leave work and (e) peaceable assembly to promote labor interest in a labor dispute. All of these union activities had, at one time or another, been declared illegal.

A second important phase of the revolution in labor law was the National Industrial Recovery Act of 1933. This act aimed to promote recovery from the depression of the time, by introducing self-regulation of business, curtailing agricultural overproduction, increasing wages, shortening the work week and raising prices. The act authorized the President to work out codes of fair competition to be voluntarily accepted by industry and to be enforced through a system of licensing. The act required employers in industries with codes of fair competition to set maximum weekly hours and minimum wage rates for employees. These codes were required to grant employees the right to organize and bargain collectively through representatives of their own choosing, free from the interference of employers and to join or assist the labor union of their own choice. It forbade the use of yellow dog contracts.

The National Industrial Recovery Act was held unconstitutional in May of 1935. In July of 1935 the National Labor Relations Act, referred to as the Wagner Act, was passed.

Section 7 of this act, patterned largely after the corresponding section of the National Industrial Recovery Act, states that:

> Employees shall have the right to self-organization, to form, join or assist labor organizations, to bargain collectively through representatives of their own choosing, and to engage in concerted activities, for the purpose of collective bargaining or other mutual aid or protection.

The act created the National Labor Relations Board to carry out the provisions of the act. Prior to this act, a union could compel an employer to recognize it only by going on strike. This act provided a new procedure for securing union recognition: a secret ballot of workers under the auspices of the Board. A union winning a majority of the votes in such an election was certified by the Board as bargaining representative. An employer's refusal to bargain collectively with the employees' certified representatives constituted an unfair labor practice.

Subsequent decisions of the Board and the courts have spelled out the obligation of the employer under this provision. He must bargain in good faith: he must give reasons for refusal to accept the union's offer; he is expected to make counterproposals; he must continue negotiations until an impasse is reached; he must sign a written agreement once terms have been agreed upon and he cannot escape his obligation to bargain by discharging his present work force and replacing them with nonmember employees.

The Act also enumerates a number of employer practices that are specified to be unfair labor practices.

In addition to refusal to bargain collectively, these include: (a) interfering with, restraining or coercing employees in the exercise of rights guaranteed in Section 7; (b) domination or interference with any labor organization; (c) to encourage or discourage membership in any labor organization by discrimination against any employee; and (d) discrimination against an employee because he has filed charges or given testimony under the act.

By its provisions the act rendered blacklisting useless. The act eliminated industrial espionage and strikebreaking as effective anti-union weapons. Even if an employer brought in strikebreakers to replace the striking employees, the striking employees, but not their replacements, were eligible to vote in elections held under the auspices of the National Labor Relations Board.

In subsequent years the National Labor Relations Board has spelled out the meaning of these provisions by specifying various anti-union acts which are unfair labor practices. An unfair labor practice is actionable at law. It can lead to court proceedings and penalties for contempt of court. Most complaints are disposed of before proceedings reach the courts, however.

These laws cover only employees of establishments engaged in interstate commerce. Many employees who were not covered by these acts were subsequently covered by "Little Wagner Acts" patterned after the Wagner Act and passed by individual states covering employees in intrastate commerce.

All these acts were important in and of themselves. They are also symptomatic of a public, legislative and executive attitude that was favorable to unions. How did this legislation and this changed social climate operate to favor union growth? One way this favorable attitude toward unions aided union growth is demonstrated by the sit-down strikes in the automobile industry.[3]

---

[3]Lloyd G. Reynolds, *Labor Economics and Labor Relations,* (First ed.), Prentice Hall, Inc., Englewood Cliffs, N.J., 1949, p. 104. Walter Galenson, *The CIO Challenge to the AFL,* Harvard Univ. Press, Cambridge, Mass., 1960, pp. 134-50.

In sit-down strikes, workers remained in the plant, but refused to work. In late 1936 and early 1937 workers in a number of automobile plants occupied the plants in sit-down strikes. This seizure and occupation of plants was widely recognized as being illegal. Automobile companies appealed to Governor Frank Murphy of Michigan to use the National Guard to evict the strikers. Violence resulted from attempts by city police in Flint, Michigan to evict strikers. Fearing additional violence and bloodshed from the use of the National Guard to evict workers, Governor Murphy refused the companies' requests and used the National Guard for policing purposes. One of their tasks was to prevent attempts at forcible eviction of the strikers. He insisted upon the use of negotiation rather than force to evict the strikers. His decisions permitted the strikers to keep the plants closed down until the union could negotiate an agreement with the companies.

The sit-down strikes broke the trail for successful unionization of the automobile industry and speeded the unionization of other industries. Governor Murphy's actions played an important role in effecting the success of sit-down strikes.

The existence of Governor Murphy's or any other administration favorable to organized labor is indicative of public opinion favorable to organized labor. Sit-down strikes received a good deal of public support.

It has been observed that it is easier to win an election than to win a strike, which was historically the only way of securing recognition. This is not the same type of recognition as that discussed earlier under organizational conditions. This refers only to recognition of a union's existence as the employees' representative organization. That previous discussion referred to recognition of an organization's ability to exercise opponent-pain power. The recognition, even though legally imposed, of an organization's existence and its right to exist does constitute one step toward recognition of an opponent's ability to exercise opponent-pain power.

Consider a union which had a good deal of op-ponent-gain power, but because of its newness and lack of treasury had little opponent-pain power. When it had to win a strike to obtain recognition as a bargaining agency, it had little chance to win recognition and to demonstrate it could help the company in some ways with its Type I power. Under the new legislation, when it only had to win an election to secure recognition as a bargaining agent, the union had an easier time of demonstrating its Type I power.

Carrying out of an election and winning recognition as a bargaining agent gave the union a psychological lift. Its existence had been sanctioned by the government; it was known to be desired by the workers. It was their union. Under these conditions it was easier to whip up sufficient support to make a strike successful than it was before when people had to strike more or less in the dark, not knowing how many supported the union nor whether the employer ever would recognize the union.

More important were the anti-injunction provisions of the laws. Quite obviously, in those conditions under which employers were able to obtain injunctions to prevent unions from interfering in any way with the employer's affairs, the union had no Type II power. Both workers and employer knew it. Tightening up on the injunction procedure meant that unions were able to exercise opponent-pain power in many situations in which injunctions would have previously interfered. The improved social climate for unions meant that any public intervention in the event of a strike was more apt to benefit the workers, whereas previously public inter-vention had favored employers.

These, plus the requirement that employers bargain in good faith, did much to increase the likelihood that a union would meet with some success. Increasing chances for success increased the workers incentive to support their unions.

The elimination of black-listing, of yellow dog contracts and of discriminatory treatment of union supporters made it much more difficult to use economic force or fear to prevent people from supporting unions or to distribute favors to those who opposed unions. Hence, many people who formerly had incentives not to support unions had this incentive removed and, as a matter of fact, replaced by incentives to support the union. Since unions could now operate in the open much more freely, it was easier than formerly to apply social pressure and moral suasion to the persons reluctant to join.

In total, this legislation contributed a great deal to the unity and stability of unions. The strength of their incentive to support the union that those people had who were satisfied with what their union was trying to accomplish, was strengthened, both because the union was more apt to succeed and because the incentive of others to support the union was strengthened. Others who would have feared to support unions now had freedom and reason to support them. Many of those who previously saw no reason for union membership now saw reasons for joining.

When we remember that this incentive to support a union is an abstract thing, easier to build up than to tear down, we see how important all this was. The strength of an individual's incentive to refuse to support an organization is reinforced by the knowledge that others have similar incentives. The strength of an individual's incentive to support an organization is weakened by this same knowledge. Provisions such as those contained in the acts can be very important in building support.

The impact of this legislation shows up in the growth of labor union membership. It also shows up in the changing composition of labor unions. In 1932, there were 155 national labor unions with three million members. Eighty percent of these unions with 85 percent of the members were craft or amalgamated craft unions. By 1952 some two-thirds of union members were in industrial, multi-industrial or industrial type unions.

The naturally greater unity of interest of workers in craft unions and their higher economic status were mentioned as reasons why craft unions were of greater importance than industrial unions in the early 1930's. The growth of union membership and the changing composition of the labor union movement is indicative of at least two things:

1. Labor legislation of the 1930's permitted large, strong industrial unions to grow in spite of the diversity of interests and backgrounds among the members. To a significant extent, the laws were a substitute for unity.

2. The operation of the laws, especially the union certification proceedings under the National Labor Relations Board, made it possible for unions to operate with less financial strength than they formerly needed.

Taft-Hartley Act

Figure 8.1 shows that union membership grew rapidly between 1933-1947. Since 1947 its rate of growth has slowed down. Figure 8.2 shows the proportion of nonagricultural employees who are union members has changed little since 1947. The growth in union membership since 1947 has been mainly due to growth in the labor force.

There are many reasons why the rate of union growth has slowed down since World War II. One reason is the passage of the Taft-Hartley Act in 1947. This act does the following, among other things:

1. As the Wagner Act lists unfair employer practices, Taft-Hartley lists unfair union practices. It places an obligation upon unions as well as upon employers to bargain collectively. Unions may not try to cause employers to discriminate against nonunion members.

2. It outlaws the closed shop, in which an employer may hire no one except union members.

3. It furnishes a procedure whereby, under the auspices of the National Labor Relations Board, employees may hold an election to vote out a union they no longer want to represent them.

4. The act makes secondary boycotts an unfair labor practice. In secondary boycotts the union exerts pressure on one employer (say employer A) to get him to exert pressure on another employer (employer B), whose workers the union wants to organize. The union may strike the employer A or may refuse to work for him using products sold to him by employer B. Up until 1947, this device was often used successfully by unions in organizing drives.

5. The act allows management the right to replace strikers by other workers and makes the replaced strikers inelegible to vote and the new workers eligible to vote in elections held to determine whether workers want to retain the union as their bargaining representative.

6. The act liberalizes the rights of employers to combat unions.

There is no general agreement among experts on the labor movement as to how great an effect the Taft-Hartley Act has had in deterring union growth. There appears to be general agreement, however, that it has been a responsible factor in causing some union organizing efforts to fail.[4] The act does not appear to have significantly weakened those unions which were established before the act was passed. The act may have made it more difficult to organize unions in those areas where unions did not exist before, especially in small towns and in the South. It may also have made it more difficult to organize unions in industries in which employees were previously not organized.

In the National Industrial Recovery Act, the Wagner Act, and others, the federal government took positive steps to aid one group in society: labor. In the Taft-Hartley Act the federal government took action to regulate this same group to protect the public welfare. Several states which passed "Little Wagner Acts" to aid labor

---

[4] Harold W. Davey, "The Operational Impact of the Taft-Hartley Act Upon Collective Bargaining Relationships," in *New Dimensions in Collective Bargaining,* (Harold W. Davey, Howard S. Kaltenborn and Stanley H. Ruttenberg, eds.), Harper and Bros., New York, 1959, pp. 184-87.

also passed "Little Taft-Hartley Acts," some before 1947, to restrict labor. This is not the first case nor is it the last, in which a government acts to promote the welfare of one group and, simultaneously or later, acts to control or restrict this group to protect the public welfare.

Starting in the middle of the last century, public land was granted to railroads to stimulate railroad construction and federal government bonds were issued to raise money to meet construction costs. In 1887 the federal congress passed a law establishing controls on railroad rate-making and forming the Interstate Commerce Commission.

At one time or another many cities have granted a monopoly to a local gas, telephone or electrical company by issuing it a franchise. Almost invariably these companies have sooner or later been subjected to public regulation as public utilities.

WHAT AGRICULTURE CAN LEARN FROM UNION EXPERIENCE

In some ways farm bargaining associations are now in the same situation labor unions were in in 1930. In 1932, craft or amalgamated craft unions dominated the labor movement. Industrial unions were a small part of the labor movement. A craft union local corresponds to an association of growers of specialized crops or of fruits or vegetables grown in one or a few localities. The two are similar in that each covers a relatively small geographic area. Members of each share a relatively strong common interest. A fairly small organization can be quite effective: small in relation to the size necessary for most industrial unions or farm bargaining associations. Members of each are engaged in the same activity.

With one exception our present bargaining associations in agriculture are confined to specialty crops, fruits and vegetables and grade A milk. These are the associations which correspond to craft unions. They have a relatively long history of operation.

Industrial unions correspond to associations of growers of products raised in widely dispersed areas: hogs, beef, corn, wheat and manufacturing milk, to name a few. Each covers a large geographic area and must be large to be effective. Industrial unions include members performing widely diverse operations. Members of associations involving these farm products would also perform widely diverse operations, since methods of production and marketing vary widely and the members raise other products.

From the history of labor unions one might reasonably expect two things:

1. Until appropriate legislation is enacted in Washington that will do for farm bargaining associations what the Norris- LaGuardia and Wagner Acts did for labor unions, the formation of strong, enduring associations representing growers of products grown in widely dispersed areas will be a slow, painful process requiring decades.

2. The enactment of appropriate legislation will greatly speed up the process. It is likely that the growers of many of these products will not have effective bargaining agencies until such legislation is enacted.

Legislation could do such things as:

1. Establish a National Agricultural Bargaining Board with duties and responsibilities similar to those of the National Labor Relations Board.

2. Provide for elections to be held under the auspices of the NABB for a group of farmers to select the bargaining association, if any, they want to represent them.

3. Provide for certifying the associations winning these elections as bargaining agents and require buyers to bargain in good faith with certified bargaining agents.

4. Grant appropriate income tax status for certified bargaining agents.

5. Provide for association dues' checkoffs to assure financial stability to certified bargaining associations.

6. Extend marketing orders to cover additional products.

MARKETING ORDERS

The extension of marketing orders to cover additional farm products would be one step which might stimulate the growth of national or regional bargaining associations.

Quality Control

Marketing orders may contain quality control provisions such as grade, size or maturity standards. Such provisions can be used to adapt output to consumers' preferences or to the needs of large scale marketing firms.

These provisions operate by prohibiting handlers from shipping to market those products which do not meet specified standards. If they cannot ship them, they probably will not buy them from farmers. Hence, a side effect of these provisions is to reduce the volume of marketings. This enhances price. Such provisions fall more heavily on some producers and handlers than on others and may even force some to leave the industry.

Volume Regulation

There are two different types of volume regulations, either or both of which may be included in a marketing order. One regulates the intraseasonal or interseasonal flow of product to the market. This type of regulation may be used to stabilize rate of marketings to prevent market gluts and subsequent price breaks. It might also be the mechanism which permits producers to take advantage of seasonal variations in demand in order to increase their revenue.

A second type of volume regulation involves surplus pooling. This operates by diverting part of the season's output to a surplus pool and disposing of the surplus in export markets or welfare programs or other markets which are noncompetitive with regular sources of demand. The burden of surplus removal to the low-priced markets is apportioned among the members. The previous discussion of demand and supply of hogs illustrates a situation in which this operation might be used. In Table

4.1, in the second year, there is a surplus of 4.1 million pigs. If price is to be maintained at $17.50 (which is the negotiated price), these 4.1 million pigs must be diverted into a surplus pool to be disposed of in supplementary markets.

The amount of farm products that can be disposed of in noncompetitive supplementary markets is severely limited. The turkey order voted upon in 1962 contained provisions for a surplus pool. Noncompetitive markets for turkeys would be the domestic off-season market, the foreign commercial market, government purchases for foreign aid, school lunch and military uses, animal and pet food and turkey specialty items. The possibilities for increasing total returns to turkey growers by selling surplus pool turkeys in these markets appear to be insignificant compared to the probable costs of turkey marketing order administration.[5]   There is no reason to believe that large supplementary markets exist for other livestock products. This country has not been able to utilize large proportions of our surplus corn and wheat in such markets.

This means that care must be exercised in using orders to raise prices. High prices could stimulate such a rapid increase in output that more products would have to be diverted into the surplus pool than could be disposed of.

It is for this reason that some federal marketing orders limit the amount of product each handler can market. Since firms are not going to buy more than they can market, this provision in effect, limits the amount that will be purchased from farmers. The turkey marketing order which was voted upon by growers in 1962 was unique in one respect. It contained provisions which would have permitted the imposition of limits on the number of turkeys each grower could sell during the marketing year. It was the first order which carried

---

[5] W. R. Henry and A. P. Stemberger, *Economic Analysis of the Proposed National Turkey Marketing Orders,* North Carolina State College, Dept. of Agr. Econ., Mis. Pub. 3, 1962.

these restrictions beyond the handler to the producer. There was some question as to whether this was legal under the act current in 1962 which authorized marketing orders. This order was rejected by the turkey growers in the referendum.

Federal milk marketing orders have two distinctive features. (1) They establish a mechanism for computing minimum prices to farmers. There is, however, no guarantee that this minimum price will be satisfactory to farmers. Other orders do not contain this provision. (2) They place no restrictions on the total quantity of product each handler can process.

Relation of Marketing Orders to Bargaining Power

We can look at orders in either of two ways. They are a substitute for bargaining power since they may be used to accomplish the same things bargaining power might be used for. They may be used to enhance farm incomes by bringing about quality improvements or by regulating seasonal flow of marketings. These are things that might be accomplished by opponent-gain bargaining power.

Some economists equate bargaining power with control of supply. If the provisions in the turkey order which could have been used to restrict the output of each turkey grower are legal, orders are a means of controlling supply without having a bargaining association. If these provisions are not legal under the present law, they can be made legal by an act of Congress.

An order can also be looked at as serving as a substitute for some of the organizational conditions. An order may be put into effect if two-thirds of the producers of a product or the producers of two-thirds of the output vote for it. It may be terminated if more than half the producers, who produce more than half the volume, request its termination. So long as it is in effect it has the force of law and violators can be punished at law.

An order is a substitute for organizational unity. If only 55 percent of the producers support an organization it will not be long successful. The support of 55 percent is sufficient to assure the existence of an order after it is once voted in. Two-thirds of the producers may not be a sufficient majority to form a stable bargaining association. This is a sufficient majority to obtain a marketing order.

An order is a substitute for the last two organizational conditions: obtaining recognition from the opponent that the organization possesses bargaining power; and ability and willingness of the members to pay the price of exerting opponent-pain power. In this sense, a marketing order can serve the same function for farmers that the National Labor Relations Act performed for labor unions in establishing the National Labor Relations Board. The act made it easier for unions to obtain recognition and in some cases eliminated the necessity for its exercising opponent-pain power before it was mature enough to be able to do so.

SUMMARY

1. Labor unions began their period of greatest growth only after the social and political climate was favorable to them and after legislation was passed which made it easier for unions to meet the conditions an organization must meet to be strong.

2. Farm bargaining associations will not sustain a rapid rate of growth until appropriate legislative or administrative action is taken to stimulate their growth.

3. One step which would promote agricultural bargaining power would be the expansion of marketing orders to cover more farm products.

4. Orders are one means of granting farmers bargaining power since they can be used to control supply. Orders also serve as a substitute for satisfying the organizational conditions.

CHAPTER 9

Determinants of Outcome of Negotiations[1]

THE AGREEMENT finally arrived at in negotiations usually represents a compromise somewhere between the positions preferred by the parties to the negotiations. The factors that determine what the outcome will be can be discussed under six broad headings:

1. Zero-profit limits
2. Consequences of doing too well
3. Consequences of a stalemate
4. Ability to withstand and inflict losses during stalemate
5. Toughness, i.e., unwillingness to yield in a situation in which the other party is expected to yield if you refuse to yield
6. Knowledge and perception.

Bargaining power was defined as the ability to bargain with influence to bring about a desired change. Since these six items determine the outcome — the amount

---

[1] This discussion draws heavily upon William Fellner, *Competition Among the Few,* Alfred A. Knopf, New York, 1949, pp. 24-33; and Stanley Siegel and Lawrence C. Fouraker, *Bargaining and Group Decision Making,* McGraw-Hill, New York, 1960.

of desired change brought about — we can say that an organization's bargaining power is determined by them.

ZERO-PROFIT LIMITS

There is evidently a lower limit to the price which a seller can afford to accept. This is his zero-profit price; if the price were any lower than this he would be losing money. There is also an upper limit to the price the buyer can afford to pay: his zero-profit price. If the price were higher than this he would be losing money.

If the highest price the buyer can afford to pay is below the lowest price the seller can afford to accept, no agreement is possible since both would be losing money. From here on we will deal with the situation in which the buyer's upper limit is above the seller's lower limit, since this is the situation in which bargaining may be important. The negotiated price will evidently be somewhere between these zero-profit limits.

The exercise of opponent-gain power is related to shifts in the zero-profit limits of the firms. As a matter of fact, when a party exercises this type of power, it is shifting the other party's zero-profit limits in a direction that is favorable to the other party. If the seller exercises opponent-gain power, he is making it possible for the buyer to raise the price he can pay the seller and still break even.

The installation of bulk tanks by all members of a dairy farmers' cooperative was cited as an example of Type I power. If a dairy receives its milk in bulk, it can reduce its costs of operation. The price it can afford to pay to farmers and still break even is now higher than it was. The farmer's costs may be lower with a bulk tank facility than they were with a can handling facility. In this case his zero-profit price is lower. The farmer's costs may be higher with a bulk tank facility. His zero-profit price will then be higher than before.

Regardless of what it does to the zero-profit limits of the party exercising Type I power, it shifts the other party's zero-profit limits in a direction favorable to him.

It was mentioned earlier that the possession of Type I power would be desirable, though perhaps not necessary. It can now be seen that there may be conditions under which the possession of Type I power is necessary; situations in which the possession of Type II power alone will not be enough to assure farmers of gains from bargaining. This will be the case if the processor or marketer of farm products is not making any money at present prices with his present operations, even though he is operating efficiently. In a case like this, a farm organization possessing opponent-pain power will be unable to get anything for its members unless it can exercise opponent-gain power to raise the firms zero-profit buying price.

CONSEQUENCES OF DOING TOO WELL

This item serves mainly to set limits to what either party may insist upon or attempt to obtain. A firm that is "too successful" is likely to be regarded by the public, the legislators, the Federal Trade Commission or by the Justice Department as taking unfair advantage of its bargaining opponent. This can lead to public criticism of and legislative restrictions on the behavior of the "too successful" firm. It can lead to judicial restriction or court action under legislation already existing. Antitrust laws are more apt to be enforced against a "too successful" monopolist than against a "reasonably successful" monopolist.

Many agree that in the years immediately after World War II this fear of consequences of faring too well did affect the pricing behavior of many large manufacturers in this country. At this time there was a tremendous backlog of demand for cars, refrigerators, furniture and other durable goods which had been unavailable during the war years. Manufacturers of these items probably could have increased prices substantially above what they did charge, without having much effect on sales. They could thereby have substantially increased their profits. They did not do this because public reaction might have been so severely critical as to lead to public control over their pricing decisions — something they wished to avoid.

The political consequences of employers faring too well appears to have played an important role in the development of labor unions in this country during the early 1930's. At that time it appears to have been generally accepted that over the years employers frequently had fared too well at the expense of the workers, that employers usually had the better of it. As a result, the public attitude toward unions was favorable and legislation favorable to labor unions was enacted.

This fear of consequences of doing too well may serve to prevent a party from realizing immediate short-term advantages which are available to it. In the case of two monopolists facing each other it may serve to make the buyer willing to pay a higher price or the seller willing to accept a lower price than if this possibility of social reaction were absent.

Any unpleasant consequences that may follow from faring too well result because people have certain ideas, vague though they may be, as to what constitutes justice and fair play and what is unfair. Actions or results that appear unfair to a large number of people will result in public retaliation. Bargainers themselves also have ideas on what is fair and what is unfair. A bargainer's conception of fair and unfair may set an upper limit to how much he will try to get out of the negotiations and also set a lower limit to how much he thinks the opponent should be able to get.

CONSEQUENCES OF A STALEMATE

Stalemate represents failure to reach an agreement. Failure to reach an agreement means cessation of production. If steel workers and steel companies fail to reach an agreement, the steel plants shut down. If grade A milk producers and bottlers reach a stalemate, a milk strike results.

The relevance of this factor varies with the importance of the industry concerned. Protracted work stoppages in important industries are generally agreed to be harmful to the public or national interest. They are almost certain to lead to public intervention of one sort or another to get production going again and to keep it going.

We have witnessed examples of this in recent years. The steel industry is frequently referred to as a basic industry, to indicate its importance to the economy. In 1959, after steel workers had been on strike for some months, a Republican administration felt it was important to put a stop to the strike. Vice President Nixon served as the President's personal representative in an effort to help steel workers and steel companies to reach an agreement. One reason why an agreement was reached shortly after his intervention was the fear on the part of each party concerned — labor and management — that if an agreement was not reached soon, more far-reaching public intervention could be expected which might react to its own disadvantage. Again, in 1962, a national administration, this time Democratic, stepped into the steel labor-management negotiations. This intervention occurred before a strike started in an effort to prevent a work stoppage.

In some cities and states, certain public employees — policemen, firemen, teachers — are prohibited by law from striking. The voters feel strongly that the normal activities of these people should not be curtailed by strikes.

At each stage of the bargaining process each party has three choices: (1) accept the other party's latest offer, (2) reject this offer and refuse to negotiate further or (3) reject this offer, but try to get more favorable terms. In what they accept, offer or reject, each party will be influenced by its best guess as to how it will fare under regulation as compared with how it will fare under the various agreements that might be reached. If both parties — seller and buyer — know that administrative regulation will significantly restrict the seller and have no effect on the buyer, this appreciably increases the buyer's bargaining power. The seller will be less willing to fight hard to obtain an agreement highly favorable to him. He will be less willing to impose a Type II loss on the buyer. It makes it likely that the price finally agreed upon will be relatively more favorable to the buyer than to the seller. And, of course, if both expect that regulation will restrict the buyer more, the negotiated price will tend to be more favorable to the seller since the buyer will be more anxious to avoid a strike or withholding action, i.e., to avoid a breakdown of negotiations.

In the absence of public intervention one party might be quite ready to choose (2) and enter into a stalemate feeling quite confident that he could ultimately beat the other party to his knees. If public intervention is likely to follow a stalemate, he must then compare how he would expect to fare under regulation with how he would expect to fare under the best agreement he can reach without forcing a stalemate. He may then decide that in the long pull he will be better off to take less now in order to avoid a stalemate and public inter-vention.

In presenting the history of labor unions it was pointed out that one reason for their rapid growth since 1932 has been the fact that any intervention by the courts and public officials is usually more favorable to unions now than before 1932, when the decisions of the courts and public officials normally favored em-ployers.

ABILITY TO WITHSTAND AND IMPOSE
LOSSES DURING STALEMATE

The fourth determinant of the bargaining outcome — ability of each party to withstand and to impose losses during stalemate — is closely related to opponent-pain bargaining power. As a matter of fact, opponent-pain bargaining power is the ability to inflict losses during a stalemate.

Stalemate, i.e., failure to reach agreement, always costs something in the short run, and the ability to with-stand these losses is a factor determining outcome. Suppose both buyer and seller know the buyer can afford a three month work stoppage, but the seller bargaining with him can afford only a one month work stoppage. The buyer will probably obtain the most favorable terms in the agreement.

One's ability to withstand losses is determined mainly by what he can afford; that is, it depends upon how much money he has to keep him going during the stalemate and to start him up after the stalemate. Herein lies the importance of the financial factor discussed in Chapter 6 under "Paying the Price."

The relative importance of the product being bargained over to the total businesses of the bargaining firms influences the ability of one party to impose losses on the other. Suppose this is the only product handled by the seller, but only 10 percent of the buyer's business depends upon this product. Then a stalemate will completely shut down the seller, but will only reduce the buyer's volume of business by 10 percent. This will place the buyer in a stronger position.

At each stage of a bargaining process, each party has the three choices listed earlier. Suppose the third choice is not available to the seller: he is unable to induce the buyer to offer more favorable terms. Then the seller's choice between (1) and (2) will be mainly determined by his estimate of the probable costs to him of (1) and (2). If the probable costs of (2), i.e., of stalemate, are greater than he can stand, he must accept (1). This is true even if the costs of (2) are less than the costs of (1). In this case the seller is forced by financial weakness to accept the more unfavorable of the two choices, i.e., the more costly of the two.

The reason for this lies in the difference between the nature of the costs of (1) and the costs of (2). A more descriptive term than costs would, perhaps, be value of lost opportunities. In evaluating the three choices, each negotiator will be calculating as best he can the effect of each choice on his income, profit and loss statement and perhaps on his balance sheet of assets and liabilities. The two largest parts of the costs of a stalemate are these: (a) lost profit opportunities because sales are not being made and (b) immediate out-of-pocket expenses such as managerial, clerical and sales personnel salaries, interest and tax payments. When a firm has no money coming in, these latter costs must be met out of money on hand.

The costs of choice number (1) are of a somewhat different nature. The main element here is the profits that will not be made if the opponent's latest offer is accepted, that would be made if more favorable terms could be obtained. These costs cumulate slowly over time. They are not immediate, nor are they out-of-pocket expenses.

Thus, in a particular situation a firm may be faced with a cost of $1 million over the next two years if it accepts the first choice and a cost of $500 thousand if it accepts the second choice. The $1 million loss from the first choice means it will make $4 million profit instead of $5 million, which it would make if it obtained the terms it wants. The $500 thousand is composed of $50 thousand profits, which will be lost during a stalemate and $450 thousand out-of-pocket expenses that will have to be met during the stalemate. If the firm has only $300 thousand in cash and short-term credit available to it, it will have to accept the first choice even though it will ultimately cost more. If the second choice is made, bankruptcy will follow.

On the other hand, if the negotiator can afford both choice (1) and choice (2), his decision will be influenced by which one he feels he can most easily afford.

This determinant of the bargaining outcome is the one that was presented as one reason why union membership is correlated with general business conditions. Union membership is correlated with union success. A shutdown means less profit opportunity is foregone when business conditions are bad and sales are slow than when business conditions are good. A union can therefore inflict less loss by striking during depression and it is less apt to be successful.

The way in which influence is distributed within an organization of farmers influences its ability to take and to inflict losses. If a majority of the members derive a substantial part of their income from the product under negotiation they may be less able to stand a stalemate than if it constitutes a relatively small portion of their total income. Members who are established, well-to-do farmers will be able to withstand losses better than younger operators who are still paying for their land and machinery. Whether the former or the latter group is more influential will affect the organization's willingness and ability to withstand losses. More aggressive members will be more willing to withstand large losses during stalemate in order to obtain larger gains than will less aggressive members. High volume, low-cost producers who can make out all right at fairly low prices will be less willing to support a stalemate in an effort to obtain higher prices than will low volume, higher-cost producers.

A bargaining association does not consist of members, each of whom is like every other member. Different members have different attitudes and preferences and operate under different conditions. The composition of membership and the characteristics of the most important group of members will influence the organization's willingness and ability to take and to inflict losses during stalemate.

TOUGHNESS

The next group of items affecting the outcome of a bargaining process is toughness. In *Competition Among the Few,* Fellner defines this as the degree of unwillingness to yield when the other party is expected to yield if you refuse to do so.

If the first four factors are correctly appraised by both parties, the range within which the negotiated price will fall is considerably narrower than the range between the zero-profit limits. The outcome then depends upon each party's appraisal of his opponent's toughness as compared with his own toughness. If both parties do not correctly appraise the first four determinants, there develops an interrelationship between each party's toughness and his appraisal of these four determinants. This interrelationship will be discussed more fully under "Knowledge and Perception."

A party's toughness will be influenced by his aspiration level. Aspiration level refers to one aspect of a person's behavior when faced with a task in which his degree of achievement can be measured. A person's aspiration level is the particular goal which he strives to attain. For example, suppose a student is preparing for an examination in a history course. His level of achievement will be measured by his grade, which may run from 0 as the lowest possible grade to 100 as the highest possible grade. If this student is trying to study enough to obtain a grade of at least 75 to 80, this grade of 75 to 80 is his aspiration level. Aspiration level is a measure of how well an individual tries to do.

Aspiration level, in turn, is affected by other forces. A prime force in determining a person's aspiration level is his past experience. Successful experiences usually lead to a raising of the aspiration level; failure usually leads to a lowering of the aspiration level. Of two bargainers, the one who has most commonly succeeded in whatever he tried to do will tend to have a higher aspiration level than the one who has failed more often in whatever he tried to do. One's aspiration level is also affected by his expectation of success. As one's expectation of success increases or decreases, his level of aspiration commonly is raised or lowered. If, as the history student studies more, he becomes confident that he can get a better grade than 80, he may raise his aspiration level to 85.

Since a bargainer's aspiration level is affected by the degree of success expected, level of aspiration can vary during bargaining negotiations. In some experimental studies of bargaining, the following behavior was observed. Occasionally one negotiator would make an unexpectedly generous offer. (It was not always intended to be generous, but by the nature of the bargaining situation it turned out that way.) The opponent's usual reaction was to increase his demands. His next offer would be one which would yield him a larger gain than his previous offer would have. He raised his aspiration level in response to an increased expectation of success. Bargaining situations have also been observed in which a reduction in the level of success expected resulted in a reduction in the level of aspiration. What one accomplishes tomorrow is affected by his level of aspiration tomorrow. Tomorrow's level of aspiration is affected by how well he does today and how well he expects to do tomorrow. Level of aspiration is influenced by the amount of information a bargainer possesses. Generally a less well-informed bargainer is apt to be more unrealistically optimistic in his expectations than is a better-informed bargainer. The possession of more information and more accurate information tends to reduce one's maximum expected pay-off because it makes expectancies more realistic. As it reduces maximum expected pay-off, it reduces the level of aspiration.

A bargainer with a high level of aspiration will be a comparatively tough bargainer because of his reluctance to make concessions in the neighborhood of his aspiration level. He will be reluctant to make concessions which would bring his share below his aspiration level. A high aspiration level for the seller would mean a high price. A high aspiration level for the buyer would mean a low price. Negotiations sometimes cover other dimensions in addition to price or quantity. Then aspiration levels will include other things in addition to price.

A bargainer with a high aspiration level will receive a larger share of the bargaining gains than a bargainer with a relatively low aspiration level, provided both are equally realistic in their aspiration levels. This proviso is important because of its relation to panic behavior. During lengthy negotiations one's aspiration level may change several times. A bargainer who has to lower his level of aspiration several times may reach his minimum level of aspiration. If it then appears he will not be able to attain even this, he is faced with two unpleasant choices. If he continues to insist on achieving this level, a stalemate will probably result. He may lower his minimum level of aspiration. Lowering one's minimum level of aspiration is likely to result in "saving what I can from a bad situation" behavior. This amounts to rapid or complete concession to the opponent: panic behavior. This is more apt to befall a party whose initial aspiration level is high and unrealistic, than a party whose aspiration level is high and realistic. The selection of realistic or unrealistic aspirations is significantly conditioned by the amount and quality (or correctness) of information a party has.

The National Labor Relations Act created the National Labor Relations Board and established new procedures for obtaining union recognition. This, along with other sections of the act and the favorable social climate, tended to give union members and leaders more expectation of success. This in turn made them tougher which, in turn, made them more successful in their bargaining efforts.

KNOWLEDGE AND PERCEPTION

This last group of items is intimately related to toughness. One's own toughness is conditioned by the toughness he expects others to exhibit. The toughness he attributes to others is conditioned by his appraisal of the first four determinants discussed in this chapter.

Suppose two monopolists are bargaining with each other. Suppose both know that the buyer can afford to pay anything up to $2.50 (his zero-profit limit) and the seller can afford to accept any price above $1.50 (his zero-profit limit). Suppose both also know that: (a) any public intervention following a long stalemate will favor the buyer over the seller and (b) the buyer can afford a longer stalemate than the seller. Then the buyer will be a tougher bargainer than the seller.

On the other hand, if the seller believes intervention will favor him and he can stand a longer stalemate, then he too will be a tough bargainer. In this last situation they cannot both be right. By the time the mistaken one finds out he is wrong, he may be bankrupt or subject to strict governmental regulation or forced into panic behavior.

Other examples could be presented to illustrate the relation between toughness and one's perception of the first four determinants.

It was pointed out previously that the possession of additional information commonly reduces one's aspiration level since it usually makes his level of expected success more realistic and less optimistic. It need not necessarily make him less tough. The possession of complete and accurate information increases one's confidence in the soundness and realism of his level of aspiration and causes him to be more reluctant to make concessions which would bring his achievements below his aspiration level.

What kinds of information are relevant? Information on:

(a) How well or how poorly each bargainer satisfies the internal organizational conditions listed previously as requisites to a sound bargaining organization.

(b) How far each party can go without creating public enmity for itself, because it is taking advantage of the other party.

(c) What the political consequences of a stalemate will be.

(d) Those conditions which determine each party's ability to take and to inflict losses during stalemate.

(e) Those forces which condition each party's toughness.

(f) Zero-profit limits of each party.

(g) Cost and profit situation of each party and supply and demand conditions.

(h) The alternatives open to each party in case no bargain is reached.

These items are not mutually exclusive. Some knowledge relevant to (g) will also be relevant to (f). Knowledge relevant to (f), in turn, will also be relevant to (e).

Ralph Bunje, general manager of the California Peach Canning Association, an association of peach growers, has pointed out the need for sound information. He has listed seven conditions for "a good climate for bargaining." One of them is:[2]

> Dealing with *FACTS* so important   to
> our long-range progress. Trying to deal with
> rumors, allegations, ideas that have no factual
> basis, only leads to weaken the bargaining
> process. Good, sound, economic *facts* can be
> the real basis upon which strong bargaining
> associations can be established.

In this chapter, perception means the ability of a negotiator to learn by observing the behavior of the other negotiators. It is primarily a psychological characteristic. Toughness was defined as a degree of unwillingness to yield when the other party is expected to do so. Perception will help one to identify those areas in which an opponent is apt to yield, those in which he is not apt to yield and those in which he will yield under sufficient pressure.

This perception is the same thing a consistently successful poker player must possess. A poker player knows what cards he has and the ranking of winning hands. He does not know what cards the opponents have. A good poker player will be able consistently to form fairly accurate impressions of what other players have by observing their behavior, especially their betting behavior, and comparing this with their behavior in past hands in which he knows what they had.

Perceptiveness is related to bluffing. When a poker player bluffs, he attempts to mislead the other players by behaving in a way which will convince them he has a stronger or weaker hand than he actually has. More perceptive players will be bluffed less often than less perceptive players.

Thus, we see that perceptiveness is related to information. It is an ability to glean accurate information by observing and comparing the opponent's behavior and to reject the misleading information he tries to pass

[2] Ralph B. Bunje, "Improving the Climate for Price Negotiation," *Proceedings of the 4th National Conference on Fruit and Vegetable Bargaining Cooperatives,* Jan. 4, 1960, USDA Farmer Coop. Serv.

out by bluffing. One's perceptiveness is affected by the amount of information he has before bargaining starts. The amount we can learn by observing a person's behavior is conditioned by what we know about him before we start observing.

RELATION OF DETERMINANTS TO ORGANIZATIONAL CONDITIONS

The organizational conditions discussed previously have a direct bearing on these determinants of the outcome of a bargaining process. Control of supply affects ability to inflict losses during stalemate. Unity and financial ability affect ability to inflict and to withstand losses during stalemate. Toughness is influenced by unity and by ability to pay the price of inflicting opponent-pain power.

SUMMARY

1. The zero-profit limits of the firms involved in bargaining are one factor determining the outcome of negotations. The exercise of opponent-gain power affects the zero-profits limits.

2. A negotiator's behavior will be conditioned by what he anticipates public reaction will be if he is too successful.

3. The anticipated consequences of a stalemate are relevant. The anticipation of unfavorable public or political consequences will cause a negotiator to settle for less than he would demand if the consequences of stalemate were expected to be favorable to him.

4. Ability and willingness to take and to inflict losses during stalemate is affected by financial factors, tightness of control of supply, and organizational unity. Ability to inflict losses is the possession of opponent-pain power.

5. Toughness depends upon one's knowledge of the variables in 1 to 4, aspiration level, knowledge and perception. A tough bargainer will usually be more successful than one who is not tough.

6. The knowledge and perception of the negotiators affects the outcome.

7. The organizational conditions discussed earlier contribute to bargaining strength through their influence on the determinants of the outcome of negotiations.

8. The bargainers' estimates of public opinion, legislation and the courts all play a significant role in determining the outcome of negotiations.

CHAPTER 10

Changes in Union Structure

IN Chapter 8 it was mentioned that industrial unions now contain a larger portion of union members than 20 or 30 years ago. Along with the growing relative importance of industrial-type unions and the relative decline of craft unions there has occurred a movement toward the formation of more amalgamated unions, multi-industrial unions and mixed craft and industrial unions.

In some cases, several craft unions, whose members perform similar work or use similar materials, will combine into one amalgamated craft union. Thus we have the International Association of Marble, Slate and Stone Polishers, Rubbers and Sawyers, Tile and Marble Setters' Helpers and Marble Mosaic and Terazzo Workers' Helpers. In other cases, unions from several related or overlapping industries will consolidate into one union. An example is the United Automobile, Aircraft and Agricultural Implement Workers of America. (This is the complete name of the United Automobile Workers.)

In other cases unions organized along industrial lines will contain some locals of craft union type. There have been many cases in which unions have signed agreements calling for cooperative action in organizing campaigns and in bargaining with and striking employers.

In general terms we can say that these structural changes represent union attempts to maintain or increase bargaining power. In specific terms, we can relate these changes to the organizational conditions of Chapter 6 and to the determinants of bargaining outcome in Chapter 9.

One reason for mergers and consolidations is the pure advantage of size. The larger treasury possessed by a large organization gives it certain advantages. (1) One determinant of the outcome of negotiations is knowledge and perception. Obtaining and interpreting the needed information will in some instances require the services of specialists. These specialists can be afforded by large organizations but not by small ones. (2) Unions sometimes face court action which may affect their ability to withstand or inflict loss. The expenses of legal counsel and court action may be beyond the financial ability of a small organization. (3) Public opinion may play a role in determining the outcome of negotiations. Unions, therefore, sometimes find it desirable to try to influence public opinion through sponsoring advertisements to present their case to the public. An effective public relations effort may require substantial expenditures of money. (4) A large union representing workers from various firms may be in much better position to afford the cost of exercising opponent-pain power. Thus, while employees of Ford are on strike, employees of General Motors, Chrysler and American Motors will continue to work and pay dues. This permits the United Auto Workers to pay strike benefits to Ford employees for a long time. If the only members of the union were Ford employees, the union could not afford to pay strike benefits to Ford workers for as long a time.

One reason for merger is the need for unity among workers to sustain strikes against a common employer. If one employer's workers are divided up among several different unions, the employer may be able to play off one union against another and use his contract with the weakest union to set limits to what the stronger unions can get. In this case, members of all unions representing his workers may gain by merging the unions. If one employer's workers are divided up among several unions, no one union may be able to shut down more than a small part of the total business. If the several unions merge they can impose greater Type II loss by completely shutting down the employer's business.

Merger can contribute to organizational unity. A strong organization needs unity and disciplinary power over its members. Sometimes a union local may strongly disagree with a decision made by the national union to which it belongs. If its national union is in competition with another national union, the local may simply switch its allegiance to the other national union. The existence of such a situation certainly limits the bargaining power of the first national union. If the two national unions merge or sign an agreement, the local no longer has this option and the national union to which the local belongs is strengthened.

Some of the changes which have taken place in the structure of the labor movement have represented union adaptation to labor mobility. Many technological advances have increased worker mobility by making more alike jobs which had been quite different. This increased ability of workers to move from occupation to occupation creates more competition for available jobs in much the same way that the development of refrigerated bulk tank trucks increased the mobility of grade A fluid milk and increased the alternative sources of supply available to any bottler. In order to maintain their control and restraint on competition for jobs, unions have had to diversify their membership base. They have done this in various ways. One way has been to organize workers in related jobs or industries that were not unionized. Sometimes this has required a craft union to become an amalgamated craft union, an industrial union (United Automobile Workers) to become a multi-industrial union (United Automobile, Aircraft and Agricultural Implement Workers of America), an amalgamated craft or an industrial union to become a mixed amalgamated craft-multi-industrial union.

The International Association of Machinists furnishes one good example.[1] During its first 45 years or so, it was essentially a craft union. During the 1930's it took some steps toward organization on an industrial basis. The movement toward industrial organization was tremendously accelerated during World War II. As a result of the need for high levels of production, many jobs formerly done by skilled craftsmen were taken over by machines with a resultant blurring of the distinction between skilled and unskilled workers. As the distinction between skilled and unskilled labor became less meaningful, the union had to switch from a craft organization to an industrial union.

The Machinists now have eight types of local unions.[2] Four represent separate industries: airframe, air transport, auto repair and railroads. One type—the tool and die local—is craft oriented as it contains members with a special skill. The production worker local contains mainly unskilled workers in mass production industries. Two other types are mixtures, neither strictly craft nor strictly industrial but a mixture of craft and industrial.

When the technological advance has increased the mobility of workers who were already organized, the result has frequently been increased jurisdictional strife. Jurisdictional disputes may bring down public disfavor on unions, and invite regulation by public agencies. Efforts to avoid jurisdictional disputes take the direction

---

[1] Mark Perlman, *The Machinists: A New Study in American Trade Unionism,* Harvard Univ. Press, Cambridge, Mass., 1961.

[2] Perlman, *Ibid.,* pp. 208-9.

of merger between the contending unions or of agreements defining the jurisdiction of each union.

Labor mobility makes it difficult for a union to maintain cohesion unless it is broadly organized. The International Association of Machinists originally was conceived as a union of railroad machinists. This policy worked fine so long as the union restricted its organizational efforts to towns in which railroads were the only employers of machinists. When the union began to move into towns where there were other employers, it had to abandon its "railroad machinists only" policy. In these towns, laid-off railroad machinists could find jobs with other employers; machinists laid off by these could get jobs with railroads.[3] If the Machinists had retained their policy of organizing only railroad machinists, they would have faced two distinct problems. (1) Every time a machinist left the railroads for another employer, the union would have lost a member; every time a machinist came to the railroads from another employer, the union would have faced the job of recruiting him as a member. The union would have had a continually revolving membership, with many short term and temporary members. It is difficult to build and maintain cohesion and unity under these conditions. It is much easier to build cohesion when most members are long-term permanent members. To avoid the weakening effects of a continually revolving membership, the union had to organize all machinists. (2) So long as railroad machinists were organized and other machinists in the same town were not, the nonunion wages received by the latter group tended to set a limit on the wages which the union could negotiate for its members.

At one time the Amalgamated Clothing Workers and the Journeymen Tailors' Union faced a similar problem.[4] The Amalgamated's membership was drawn from men's clothing factories. The Tailors' membership

---

3 Perlman, *Ibid.*, pp. 6-7.
4 Walter Galenson, *The CIO Challenge to the AFL*, Harvard Univ. Press, Cambridge, Mass., 1960, p. 285.

worked in and for custom tailors in retail stores. There had been jurisdictional conflict between the two organizations because of labor movement between clothing factories and the retail stores. To eliminate this jurisdictional conflict and to stabilize membership, the Amalgamated Clothing Workers absorbed the Journeymen Tailors' Union.

SUMMARY

1. Over the past several decades, the structure of the labor movement has changed considerably. There has been a trend away from pure craft or industrial unions to amalgamated craft unions, multi-industrial unions and to mixed unions containing some characteristics of craft and some characteristics of industrial unions. These trends represent efforts on the part of unions to maintain or increase their bargaining power.

2. One way these changes have been carried out is by the merger of two or more unions into one union.

3. Advantages of merger are: greater financial strength, increased opponent-pain bargaining power, fewer possibilities for jurisdictional disputes which may create public disfavor, greater stability of membership and hence greater unity and cohesion and reduced opportunity for dissident locals to switch allegiance from one national union to another.

4. Some of these advantages can also be obtained by agreements among unions, without actual mergers.

CHAPTER 11

Summary

BARGAINING POWER is the ability to negotiate or bargain with sufficient influence to bring about a desired change. There are two types of bargaining power. Type I or opponent-gain power is the ability to make the bargaining opponent better off if he accepts your offer. Type II or opponent-pain power is the ability to make him worse off if he rejects your offer and refuses to improve his own offer. Historically, farmers have rarely exercised opponent-pain power. Although they have long exercised opponent-gain power, they have by no means utilized it in all cases where they might.

When two or more parties are involved in a bargaining process, the final outcome is determined by six conditions. These, which determine bargaining power, are:

1. Zero-profit limits. For the seller this is the price below which he is losing money. For the buyer, it is the highest price he can afford to pay without losing money. The exercise of Type I power affects the zero-profit limits.

2. Consequences of doing too well. Being "too successful" may bring public, legislative or administrative retribution. A negotiator may temper his demands in order not to be "too successful."

3. Consequences of a stalemate. Stalemate may bring public, legislative or administrative intervention. In negotiations, each party's decisions will be affected by his judgment as to how such intervention will affect him as compared with how he may expect to do in the absence of intervention.

4. Ability to take and to inflict losses during stalemate. Ability to inflict losses during stalemate is Type II power. An organization's ability to take and to inflict losses is influenced by the volume of product it controls, by its unity and cohesion and by the financial strength of its members.

5. Toughness. This is unwillingness to yield in a situation in which the other party is expected to yield if you refuse to do so. This also is affected by an organization's unity and by the ability and willingness of members to pay the price of exercising opponent-pain power.

6. Knowledge and perception. The knowledge and perception of the negotiators affects outcome partly through its effect on toughness. Well-informed negotiators and well-informed membership are necessary for a successful organization.

Large size is necessary in order to control a sufficient volume of supply to exercise significant Type II power. Large size makes it difficult to attain organizational unity. This is due to the increasing heterogeneity of membership with increasing size and to problems in communication and membership participation in larger organizations. Also, members of large organizations lack the feeling of personal contribution to the success of the organization and of personal responsibility for the success of the organization, that members of small organizations possess.

The period of rapid labor union growth in this

country did not occur until after specific legislation was enacted which increased the unity and cohesion of unions. It made it easier for them to exercise opponent-pain power and made the immediate political consequences of stalemate more favorable to unions.

Large, e.g., statewide, regional or national, farm bargaining organizations will find it extremely difficult to enhance farm income over long periods of time until they are the beneficiaries of favorable legislation or administration, as the unions were. Smaller associations are severely limited in what they can achieve since they control a small proportion of total supply.

A business will find it easier to grant gains to farmers if they are earned by the exercise of opponent-gain power than if they are obtained through the exercise of opponent-pain power. The former type allows the business to pay higher prices or grant other gains to farmers while the business remains as well-off as before. Type II gains are not similarly painless.

Type II gains may come out of present marketing costs or out of the pockets of consumers. If farmers accompany the higher prices charged consumers with an improved product or an improved timing or method of marketing, both farmers and consumers can be better-off. To try to charge higher prices without changing production or marketing methods will bring farmers face to face with the law of demand. Over the years population growth and rises in consumer income tend to increase the demand for farm products. Raising prices faster than warranted by this growth in demand results in reductions in consumer purchases. Hence, organizations that negotiate substantial increases in prices are going to find the sales of their members falling sharply. Since higher farm prices tend to bring about increases in farm output, this decline in sales will occur simultaneously with an increase in the amount farmers produce for market.

This simultaneous decline in sales and rise in production will present a bargaining association with a severe test of its unity. To maintain price, it will be necessary for members to voluntarily cut back production. If the members insist on freedom to produce all they want to, the negotiated price cannot be maintained. It is difficult, and probably impossible, to form a large organization possessing sufficient unity to be able to survive this test. Legally imposed production controls, e.g., through national or regional marketing orders, would relieve the organization of the necessity of facing this test.

Because of the relation between high price and low volume of purchases by consumers and the relation between high price and high production, some people have treated bargaining power as being synonymous with power to curtail supply. Ability to curtail supply means ability to limit it to that volume which can be sold at the desired price.

Demand at the farm level can be increased either through population and income growth or through reductions in costs of marketing. The opportunities for farmers to obtain higher prices by forcing reductions in marketing costs are quite modest. Two opportunities lie in reducing profits of marketing and processing firms and reducing the wages and salaries paid to employees of these firms. The gains obtainable from these two sources are not sufficient to raise farm prices by more than a few percent on the average. Higher prices to farmers may also be financed by increased efficiency forced on marketing firms in order to pay higher prices to farmers. On the average, farmers may not be able to get much by cutting marketing costs. But some highly efficient firms may be able to finance substantially higher prices to farmers while earning better profits than their less efficient competitors. Conversely, some firms will be forced out of business if they are forced by a bargaining association to pay higher prices to farmers.

Consumer
Demand

FIGURE 3.1 (page 40) shows how annual average consumer's purchases of beef are related to annual average beef prices paid by consumers. Figure 3.2 (page 41) presents similar information for pork. In this section we see how these figures were obtained.

Along the horizontal axis in Figure A.1 is measured annual per capita beef consumption. Along the vertical axis is measured the average retail price of beef divided by an index of per capita income. Actual data are plotted for several years. For example, in 1956 per capita beef consumption was 85.4 pounds and the average retail beef price divided by an index of income was 47.2 cents. The solid line represents the average relation between adjusted price and per capita consumption in 1956-1960. Figure A.2 presents the same information for pork.

We can interpret these average relations as follows, using Figure A.1 as an example. The line indicates the highest adjusted retail price at which various per capita quantities of beef could be sold on the average in 1956-

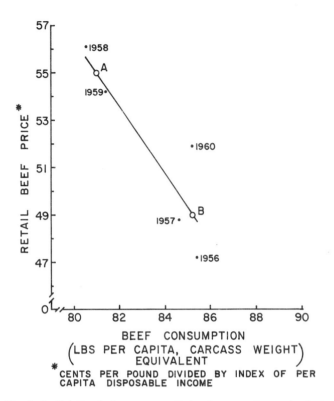

Fig. A. 1—Relation between per capita beef consumption and adjusted retail beef price, 1956-60. **Sources:** Consumption data from USDA Econ. Research Serv., 1960 Supplement to **Consumption of Food in the United States 1909-52,** Ag. Handbook 62. 1961. Table 8. Income from **Ibid.,** Table 49. Beef price from USDA Agricultural Marketing Serv. Supplement for 1961, to **Livestock and Meat Statistics,** Stat. Bul. 230, 1961.

1960; alternatively it indicates the highest levels of per capita beef sales which could be attained with various adjusted prices on the average. The lines indicate that larger volumes of per capita beef and pork consumption could be attained only by reducing price with a constant income and population. When prices were raised, per capita consumption would tend to fall.

Although Figures A.1 and A.2 use data only for the years 1956-1960, the relationships presented by the solid lines are typical of longer periods. When income and population change slowly, charging higher prices results in a decline in per capita consumption.

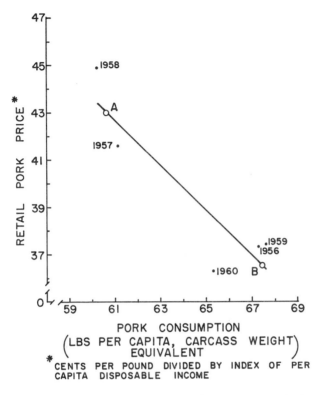

Fig. A. 2—Relation between per capita pork consumption and adjusted retail pork price, 1956-60. **Sources:** Same as Fig. A. 1.

There are a number of reasons why the points do not fall directly on the lines. Figure A.1 relates beef consumption to adjusted beef price. Beef consumption is affected by other forces in addition to beef prices and income. Broiler prices and hog prices are the two most important. If these had remained constant from 1956 to 1960, all points in Figure A.1 would fall closer to the line. Although all points do not fall exactly on the lines in the two figures, in each case when price rose from one year to the next, consumption fell and when price fell, consumption rose. The only exception is for pork, 1959-1960.

To convert the relation in Figure A.1 into the

relation between total beef consumption and actual retail beef price in Figure 3.1, we use the following procedure. (This will also illustrate how Figure 3.2 is derived from Figure A.2.) Take two points on the line in Figure A.1, say *A* and *B*. The values of adjusted price and per capita consumption at these points are presented in Table A.1. Multiplying consumption per person by number of persons gives total consumption. Average population during 1956-1960 was 174.3 million. Multiplying this figure by per capita consumption at points *A* and *B* we obtain:

174.3 million x 81.0 pounds = 14.12 billion pounds of beef consumption at adjusted price of 55 cents.

174.3 million x 85.2 pounds = 14.85 billion pounds of beef consumption at adjusted price of 49 cents.

These results are summarized on lines 1 and 2, Table A.2 and in Figure A.3. To draw Figure A.3, simply copy the vertical axis from Figure A.1 and measure billions of pounds along the horizontal axis. The points *A* and *B* indicate the computed levels of total beef consumption at the two adjusted prices. Draw a straight line between these two points.

The next step is to convert the adjusted prices at points *A* and *B* to the actual retail prices. The average value of the index of per capita income for 1956 to 1960 was 147.4. Multiply 55 and 49 (the adjusted prices at points *A* and *B*) by this figure.

147.4 x 55 cents = 81.1 cents; maximum price at which 14.12 billion pounds of beef can be sold annually.

147.4 x 49 cents = 72.2 cents; maximum price at which 14.85 billion pounds of beef can be sold annually.

Table A.1. Values of Adjusted Beef Price and Per Capita Consumption, Points A and B, Figure A.1

Point	Adjusted Price	Per Capita Consumption
	(cents)	(pounds)
A	55	81.0
B	49	85.2

Table A.2. Converting Relation Between Per Capita Beef Consumption and Adjusted Price (Fig. A.1) to Relation Between Total Consumption and Price (Fig. 3.1)

Line	Average Population	Average Index of Per Capita Income	Figure	Point	Adjusted Price	Adjusted Per Capita Consumption	Total Consumption	Price
(1)	(2)	(3)	(4)	(5)	(6)	(7)	(8)	(9)
	(millions)	(percent)			(cents/pound)	(pounds)	(billion pounds)	(cents/pound)
1	174.3		A1	A	55*	81.0*	14.12†	
2	174.3		A1	B	49*	85.2*	14.85†	
3		147.4	A3	A	55*		14.12*	81.1‡
4		147.4	A3	B	49*		14.85*	72.2‡
5			3.1	A			14.12*	81.1*
6			3.1	B			14.85*	72.2*

* Numbers plotted in the indicated figure.
† These figures = column (2) multiplied by column (7).
‡ These figures = column (3) multiplied by column (6).

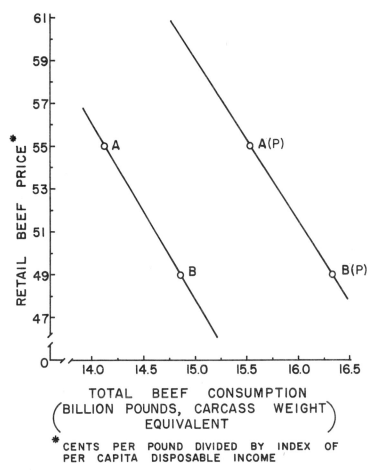

Fig. A. 3—Relation between total beef consumption and adjusted retail beef price, 1956-1960.

These are presented in lines 3 and 4, Table A.2 Points *A* and *B* in Figure 3.1 are plotted to show these combinations of price and sales. A line is drawn through these two points. With average 1956-1960 conditions this line indicates how much beef could be sold to consumers at various retail prices. It also indicates the maximum prices which could be charged at retail to sell various volumes of beef annually. This line slopes downward to the right, as is characteristic of such demand curves. This shows that more can be sold only at lower prices. Table A.3 shows how Figure 3.2 was derived from Figure A.2. Growth in population and consumer income serves to increase demand. How this operates can be shown with the aid of Figures A.1, A.3 and 3.1. Points *A* and *B* in Figure A.3 were obtained by multiplying the levels of per capita consumption at points *A* and *B* in Figure A.1 by average 1956-1960 population. Suppose average population had been 10 percent larger: 191.7 million. Multiplying the levels of per capita consumption at points *A* and *B* by 191.7, we obtain 15.53 billion pounds and 16.33 billion pounds, plotted at points *A(P)* and *B(P)* in Figure A.3. (See lines 1 to 4, Table A.4) *A(P)* corresponds to point *A*. The *(P)* indicates it differs from *A* because of the growth in population (first letter,*P*). *B(P)* is similarly interpreted.

The fact that the line through these points is to the right of and above the line through *A* and *B* can be interpreted in either of two ways. (1) At any particular adjusted price, total consumption will rise as population rises. For example, at an adjusted price of 55 cents, a 10 percent rise in population will raise total annual consumption from 14.12 billion pounds to 15.53 billion pounds. (2) Any particular total volume can be sold at higher prices as population rises. For example, a 10 percent rise in population raises the price which can be charged for 14.85 billion pounds from 49 to 60.5 cents.

Income growth has the same kind of effect on total demand as population growth has. Points *A* and *B* in Figure 3.1 were obtained by multiplying the adjusted prices at points *A* and *B* in Figure A.3 by the average index of per capita income in 1956 to 1960: 147.4. Suppose per capita income had been 10 percent higher— 162.1—and population was at its average value. Multiplying the adjusted prices at points *A* and *B* in Figure

Table A.3. Converting the Relation Between Per Capita Pork Consumption and Adjusted Retail Price (Fig. A.2) to a Relation Between Total Pork Consumption and Actual Retail Price (Fig. 3.2)

Line	Average population	Average index of per capita income	Figure	Point	Adjusted price	Per capita consumption	Total consumption	Price
(1)	(2)	(3)	(4)	(5)	(6)	(7)	(8)	(9)
	(millions)	(percent)			(cents/ pound)	(pounds)	(billion pounds)	(cents/ pound)
1	174.3		A2	A	43.0*	60.6*	10.56[†]	
2	174.3		A2	B	36.5*	67.4*	11.75[†]	
3		147.4			43.0		10.56	63.4[‡]
4		147.4			36.5		11.75	53.8[‡]
5			3.2	A			10.56*	63.4*
6			3.2	B			11.75*	53.8*

* Numbers plotted in the indicated figure.
† These figures = column (2) multiplied by column (7).
‡ These figures = column (3) multiplied by column (6).

Table A.4. Converting the Relation Between Per Capita Beef Consumption and Adjusted Price (Fig. A.1) to Relation Between Total Consumption and Price with 10 Percent Growth in Population and Income

Line	Average Population Plus 10% Growth	Average Index of Per Capita Income Plus 10% Growth	Figure	Point	Adjusted Price	Per Capita Quantity	Total Quantity	Price
(1)	(2)	(3)	(4)	(5)	(6)	(7)	(8)	(9)
	(millions)	(percent)			(cents/pound)	(pounds)	(billion pounds)	(cents/pound)
1	191.7		A1	A	55*	81.0*	15.53†	89.2‡
2	191.7		A1	B	49*	85.2*	16.33†	79.4‡
3			A3	A(P)	55*		15.53*	89.2*
4			A3	B(P)	49*		16.33*	79.4*
5		162.1	A3	A	55*		14.12*	89.2*
6		162.1	A3	B	49*		14.85*	79.4*
7			3.1	A(I)			14.12*	89.2*
8			3.1	B(I)			14.85*	79.4*
9		162.1	A3	A(P)	55*		15.53*	89.2*
10		162.1	A3	B(P)	49*		16.33*	79.4*
11			3.1	A(P+I)			15.53*	89.2*
12			3.1	B(P+I)			16.33*	79.4*

* Numbers plotted in the figure.
† These figures = column (2) multiplied by column (7).
‡ These figures = column (3) multiplied by column (6).

A.3 by 162.1 yields prices of 89.2 and 79.4 cents per pound, plotted as *A(I)* and *B(I)* in Figure 3.1.(See lines 5 to 8, table A.4.) *A(I)* corresponds to *A*. The *(I)* indicates it differs from *A* because of the growth in income *(I)*. *B(I)* is interpreted similarly. The line through *A(I)* and *B(I)* in Figure 3.1 is to the right of and above the line through *A* and *B*, indicating that income growth also raises demand for beef. It permits a higher quanity to be sold at a particular price or it permits a higher price to be received for a particular quantity.

The points *A(I)* and *B(I)* were obtained on the assumption of average 1956 to 1960 population and a 10 percent rise in income over 1956 to 1960. If population and income both had been 10 percent higher, the demand line would have been the line through points *A(P+I)* and *B(P+I)* in Figure 3.1. These are obtained by multiplying the prices at points *A(P)* and *B(P)* by 162.1, which is 10 percent above the actual average income of the period. (See lines 9 to 12, Table A.3.)

FARM LEVEL DEMAND

Since agricultural processing firms purchase from farmers in anticipation of selling to consumers, the prices that they pay to farmers and the volumes that they buy from farmers are affected by what they believe consumers will be willing to pay for the quantity and quality of product offered to them. That is, the demand for beef cattle or hogs or eggs or fresh cherries from the farmer is a derived demand. It derives from consumer demand for the products which are made from the cow or the hog or the egg or the fresh cherries.

We can use the line through *A* and *B* in Figure 3.1 to show how farm level demand is derived from consumer demand. The process is sketched out in Table A.5 and Figure A.4. During the period 1956 to 1960, farm price of beef averaged about 60 percent of the retail price of beef. Thus, the retail price of 81.1 cents, point *A* in Figures 3.1 and 3.3 (pages 40, 46) was split

81.1 x 0.60 = 48.7 cents to the farmer and the rest,
32.4 cents, to processing and marketing firms. From
this we get the point *AF* in Figure 3.3.

Together, points *A* and *AF* tell this story. At a
retail price of 81.1 cents per pound, consumers would
buy 14.12 billion pounds of beef. Since farm price is
60 percent of retail price, processors will pay 48.7 cents
for this much beef. Points *B* and *BF* say: To sell 14.85
billion pounds, retail price can be no higher than about
72.2 cents. With this retail price, farm price will be
43.3 cents.

The distance between the two lines *AB* and *AF BF*
in Figure 3.3 represents marketing margin. The earlier
discussion of marketing firms as a source of bargaining
gains can also be looked at from the standpoint of
this graph. Line *AF BF* represents farm level demand
when marketing charges run 40 percent of retail cost.
Suppose marketing charges could be cut to 30 percent;
farm price would then be 70 percent of retail price.
Farm level demand would then be represented by the
line through *AF(M)* and *BF(M)*. The point *AF(M)*
differs from *AF* because of the change in marketing
(M) costs. Thus, we see that reducing marketing costs
permits farmers to receive higher prices for the same
amount of output. By contrast, if marketing costs do
not change, charging higher prices means less will be
sold. This, remember, is the meaning of the fact that
the demand curve slopes downward to the right.

The effect of growth in income and population is,
of course, to shift the farm level demand curve upward
and to the right. In Figure A.4 the lines through *A B*
and through *AF BF* are copied from Figure 3.3. The
line through *A(P+I)* and *B(P+I)* is copied from Figure
3.1. It represents retail level demand following a 10
percent rise in income and population over their 1956-
1960 average values. If the farmer's share of the retail
price remained at 60 percent, its average 1956-1960
value, the new farm level demand curve would be the
line through *AF(P+I)* and *BF(P+I)*.

Table A.5. Derivation of Farm Level Demand for Beef from Retail Level Demand

Line	Farm Price as Proportion of Retail Price	Figure	Point	Retail Price	Total Quantity	Farm Price
(1)	(2)	(3)	(4)	(5)	(6)	(7)
				(cents/ pound)	*(billion pounds)*	*(cents/ pound)*
1	0.60	3.3	A	81.1*	14.12*	48.7†
2	0.60	3.3	B	72.2*	14.85*	43.3†
3		3.3	AF		14.12*	48.7*
4		3.3	BF		14.85*	43.3*

* Numbers plotted in the indicated figure. Points AF and BF are the same in Figure 3.3 as in Figure A.4.

† These figures = column (2) multiplied by column (5).

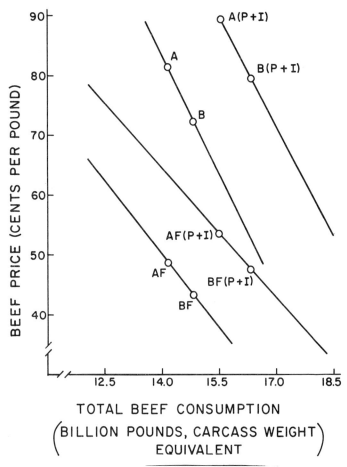

Fig. A. 4—Shift in retail level and farm level demand for beef.

If, however, the farmer's share of the retail price fell from 60 to 40 percent while income and population were growing by 10 percent, the farm level demand curve would still be the line through *AF BF*. The farm level demand curve would remain the same even while the retail level demand curve shifted. If the farmer's share of the retail price fell below 40 percent, the farm level demand curve, even after the growth in population and income, would be below the line through *AF BF*.

EFFECT OF 1950-1960 GROWTH IN

   POPULATION AND INCOME

   Figures A.5 and A.6 use the ideas presented in Figures A.3 and A.4 to show what happened to farm and retail prices between 1950 and 1960. The line in Figure A.5 labeled *50 - 50* shows consumer demand in

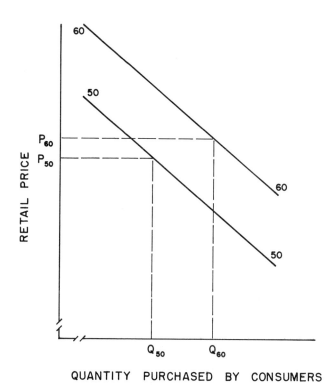

QUANTITY   PURCHASED   BY   CONSUMERS

Fig. A. 5 — Shift in retail demand between 1950 and 1960.

1950. It corresponds to the line *A B* in Figure A.4. The line *60 - 60* shows consumer demand in 1960. Income and population growth moved the demand line to the right. For livestock and livestock products, the amount of annual consumption is virtually identical with annual

production. The point Q_{50} shows the quantity purchased
and produced in 1950. The point Q_{60} shows the amount
purchased and produced in 1960. Points P_{50} and P_{60}
show average retail prices in the two years. Because of
population and income growth, demand grew enough
so that the 1960 retail price was higher than the 1950
price even though 1960 consumption exceeded 1950
consumption.

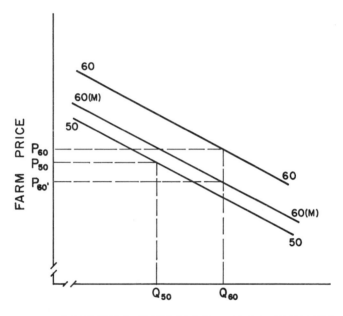

QUANTITY PURCHASED FROM FARMERS

Fig. A. 6—Shifts in farm level demand between 1950 and 1960.

In Figure A.6, the lines *50-50* and *60-60* represent
derived farm level demand. They are obtained from
Figure A.5 in the same way *AF BF* in Figure A.4 is
derived from *AB*. Thus, the line *50-50* represents actual
farm level demand in 1950; the line *60-60* represents
what farm level demand would have been in 1960 *if*
the farmer's share of the retail price had not fallen. The
points Q_{50} and Q_{60} represent volumes of farm sales

in the two years. P_{50} represents farm price in 1950 and P_{60} shows what farm price would have been in 1960 *if* marketing costs had not risen between 1950 and 1960. The line *60 (M) 60(M)* shows what the derived farm level demand actually was in 1960. (It is below the line *60 - 60* because the rise in marketing costs exceeded the rise in retail price.) The point P_{60}' then, shows what farm prices actually were in 1960.

Volume
of Farm
Production

The line through *C* and *D* in Figure 4.1 (page 56)
was presented as representing the average relation between the hog-corn price ratio of one year and the level
of hog production of the next year. We will now consider
how this line was derived.

Figure B.1 shows how the annual pig crop of one
year is affected by the hog-corn price ratio during the
previous year. This ratio is computed by dividing the
average price of 100 pounds of live hog by the price of
one bushel of corn. It shows how many bushels of corn
100 pounds of live hog will buy. Feed is an important
part of the total cost of hog production; amounting to
65 to 70 percent of total cost. Corn is the main feed and
prices of other feeds are closely related to corn prices.
Thus, the hog-corn price ratio is a measure of the profitability of hog production. As this ratio rises, hog production becomes more profitable.

In Figure B.1 the point labeled 1955 shows the
1955 pig crop to have been 96 million and the 1954
hog-corn price ratio to have been 15. The point labeled

1956 shows the 1956 pig crop to have been 89 million pigs and the 1955 hog-corn price ratio to have been 11.5. Between 1954 and 1955 the hog-corn price ratio fell; this was followed by a fall in the 1956 pig crop. Between 1955 and 1956 the hog-corn price ratio again fell, from 11.5 to 11. This was followed by a decline in the 1957 pig crop to 87 million. Between 1956 and 1957 the hog-corn price ratio rose to 15.5; this encouraged a larger 1958 hog crop of 93 million. In each case a decline in the hog-corn price ratio (i.e., the profitability of hog production) was followed by a decline in hog production and a rise in the hog-corn price ratio by an increase in hog production.

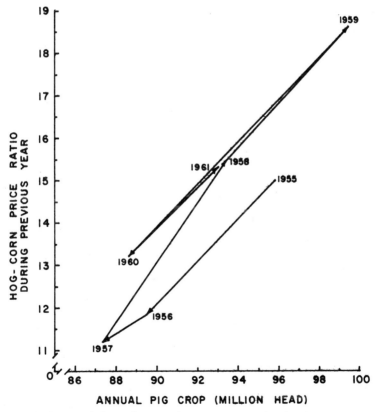

Fig. B. 1—United States hog supply in one year related to hog-corn price ratio of the preceding year, 1954-61. **Sources:** 1954-60 pig crop from Agr. Marketing Serv. Supplement for 1960 to **Livestock and Meat Statistics,** USDA Stat. Bul. 230, 1961. Table 41. Hog-corn price ratio from **Ibid.,** Table 188. 1961 pig crop from Agr. Marketing Serv. **Livestock and Meat Situation,** March 1962, Table 7.

One way of increasing the profitability of hog production is to raise the price of hogs while the price of corn remains the same. The effect of raising the price of hogs will be to reduce purchases of hogs and increase production. We can use Figures 3.2 (page 11) and B.1 to show this.

The procedure by which we can do this involves these steps:

1. Convert the line of average relation between annual pork consumption and annual average retail pork price in Figure 3.2 to an average relation between equivalent number of hogs consumed and equivalent farm price of pork. This process is shown in Table B.1. The figure of 83.3 percent in column (3) indicates that one hog averaged 120 pounds of pork. The ratio of 27.75 percent in column (2) means that the farm price of one pound of hog liveweight was nearly 28 percent of the price of one pound of pork. (Because of the units in which consumption is measured here, this means that the retail value [excluding by-products] of one pound of hog averaged slightly over 50 percent of the retail price of pork.)

The resulting points on the last two lines of Table B.1 are plotted in Figure 4.1 as points A and B.

2. Figure B.1 shows information on the hog-corn price ratio for one year and hog production the next. If we can convert this to the relation between hog price and number of hogs, this information can be plotted in Figure 3.1. To do this we first find a line of average relation between the points in Figure B.1. This line is not plotted on the figure. It goes through the two points:

(1) Hog-corn ratio = 11.75; pig crop = 87.5
(2) Hog-corn ratio = 17.00; pig crop = 96.8

The average price of corn was $1.21 per bushel during the period plotted. Multiplying 1.21 by the hog-corn ratios of 11.75 and 17.0 we obtain hog prices of $13.95 and $20.60 per hundred weight, or 13.95 and 20.6 cents per pound, for pig crops of 87.5 and 96.8 million pigs. These two points are plotted as C and D in Figure 4.1.

Table B.1. Obtaining Farm Level Demand for Hogs From Retail Level Demand for Pork

Line	Ratio of Farm to Retail Price	Ratio of Number of Hogs Produced to Pounds of Pork Produced	Retail Pork Price	Total Pork Consumption	Number of Hogs Consumed	Farm Price of Hogs	Figure	Point
(1)	(2)	(3)	(4)	(5)	(6)	(7)		
	(percent)	*(percent)*	*(cents/ pound)*	*(million pounds)*	*(million)*	*(cents/ pound)*		
1		83.3	63.4	10,560	88.0 *			
2		83.3	53.8	11,750	97.9 *			
3	27.75		63.4		88.0	17.6 [†]		
4	27.75		53.8		97.9	14.9 [†]		
					88.0	17.6	4.1	A
					97.9	14.9	4.1	B

* These figures = column (3) multiplied by column (5).

† These figures = column (2) multiplied by column (4).

Index